A
Harlequin
Romance

OTHER

Harlequin Romances

by VIOLET WINSPEAR

Many of these titles are available at your local bookseller,
or through the Harlequin Reader Service.

For a free catalogue listing all available Harlequin Romances,
send your name and address to:

HARLEQUIN READER SERVICE,
M.P.O. Box 707, Niagara Falls, N.Y. 14302
Canadian address: Stratford, Ontario, Canada.

or use order coupon at back of book.

DEAR PURITAN

by

VIOLET WINSPEAR

HARLEQUIN BOOKS   TORONTO
WINNIPEG

Original hard cover edition published in 1971
by Mills & Boon Limited, 17 - 19 Foley Street,
London W1A 1DR, England

© Violet Winspear 1971

SBN 373-01658-1

Harlequin edition published February 1973

Printed in Canada

1658

CHAPTER ONE

THE train thundered into the sunset as if it were heading for the gateway to the sun itself. A golden glow lay over the landscape and turned to purple the tips of the Mexican mountains. The wheels of the train made a rhythm to which Romy Ellyn set her own words as she sat beside the window in her private compartment and watched the flight of a great bird across the vivid sky. An eagle with outspread wings, strong enough to snatch a young animal from the *sabana*.

It was all so excitingly different from Lovtanet Bay, where Romy had spent her childhood and her growing up. There with wings as grey as the sea gulls had swooped in the sky and seals had lounged on the rocks only a short distance from the beach. To remember the bay was to think of Lance and the many happy hours they had spent in the water and the caves where long ago smugglers had stored their loot. Now he meant no more to her. He had married her cousin Iris, whose father had made a fortune from the canning of fish.

Holding on to her smile when Iris flaunted her engagement ring, Romy had agreed to be a bridesmaid, but a week after the wedding she went away to Bristol to study for a post at the Museum of Childhood, which appealed strongly to her. It wasn't long afterwards that she had to face another blow when Nonna, her grandmother, died suddenly and peacefully in her sleep. Fond of the girl who had been thrown upon the mercy of relatives at an early age, Nonna had left her a legacy, and also a letter sealed in the old-fashioned way with red wax.

When the letter was handed to Romy, she saw the instant gleam of curiosity in the eyes of her aunt and her cousin. 'Well, open it,' Iris said, blonde and pretty in her dark suit with a collar of fur. 'You and Nonna were always huddling together and whispering secrets. Perhaps she's left you a bit of country nonsense on how to catch a man.'

Romy, too upset by the loss of Nonna to care any more that her cousin's tart remarks could sting, carefully opened her letter and read it in silence. 'Each of us,' Nonna had written, 'has a longing when young to visit a faraway place. Go wandering for a while, Romy. Don't hold back, or let yourself be persuaded that the legacy I leave you should be hoarded for a rainy day. Go chase a rainbow, girl. Go with eagerness and courage, and my love.'

'Well,' Iris urged, 'what does the old girl have to say?'

'That with my legacy I'm to take a trip ... abroad.'

'And will you?' Iris shot a complacent smile at her husband Lance, as if to emphasise the fact that she had taken him away from Romy. 'Paris

6

is nice in the spring, and so is Venice. Lance and I simply adored Venice and all those romantic palaces, and you could probably find a girl-friend to go with you.'

'I shall go alone.' Romy gazed at the letter and never had she felt so sure of what she wanted. 'I shall go where it pleases me to go, and I shall spend every penny Nonna has left me. I shall buy some really smart clothes, and with the rest I shall have fun.'

'On your lonesome?' Iris drawled.

'Yes, all on my own ...' And even alone Mexico City had been fascinating beyond words, and she had visited many intriguing museums and made sketches of the costumes and playthings of Mexican children. Now by train she was bound for Xerica, where she would stay for a week, and then journey on to Vera Cruz to catch a steamer for England ... and home.

What a sunset! It was as if that golden globe had been dropped into a furnace and drawn out again. Somewhere along the train bells rang to warn the passengers who wished to dine that the meal would soon be ready.

It had been an added expense to take a private compartment, but Romy wasn't regretful. Few women seemed to travel alone, unescorted, in this part of the world, and the men had such a dark and dangerous look about them. She arose from her seat and washed her face in her private washbasin. She was no bread-and-butter miss who quaked at the knees very easily, but it gave her a sense of security to have a compartment she could lock before going to bed, and a tiny pearl-handled automatic which she had bought in Mexico City in a quaint side-street shop.

She brushed her tawny hair, which was not kept in order unless she pinned it into a large soft knot at the nape of her neck, a style which exposed her temples, the clear line of her jaw, and the smallness of her ears. Romy was a girl not formally pretty, but it showed in her features that she had pluck, tenderness, and a ready sense of humour. It still hurt a little that Lance had only been playing with her youthful feelings, but not so deeply that she couldn't enjoy the climate of Mexico, the history of its colourful people, and the quaint villages surrounding the golden churches built by the Spanish conquerors. Romy met her own eager green eyes in the wall mirror and was glad she had spent Nonna's legacy in this way. It would always be a holiday to remember; something to brighten the lonely evenings when she returned to her bed-sitter in Bristol.

Right now the train was travelling through the heart of the country, and Romy felt exhilarated and hungry as she made her way along the swaying corridor to the dining-car. A man was walking ahead of her, and there was something about his apparel, the way he carried his head and shoulders ... a supple, lordly air ... that made Romy catch her breath and slow her footsteps. She hoped he would enter the dining-car without a backward glance, but just as he reached the door he paused to gaze from the corridor window at the passing scenery bathed in the glow of the setting sun. Even as Romy was debating a hasty retreat to her compartment he must have caught a glimpse of her leaf-green dress and her tawny hair.

He swung right round to face her and after that there was no escaping him. He gave her a brief, courteous bow. 'Good evening, *señorita*.' He remembered her, as she remembered him, and she felt again that odd sense of shock as she met his bronze-coloured eyes under the level black brows, saw again those powerfully sculptured features and the skin of dark gold. The face was utterly masterful, and it belonged to Don Delgado de Avarado y Valcazar, a Consul of this country, and a man of considerable power and wealth, whose estate she had been told ran to many hundreds of acres.

'So we meet again in yet another unexpected way.' He spoke faultless English, with an accent that carved each word. 'Did you enjoy the remainder of your stay in Mexico City?'

'Very much, *señor*.' She smiled politely and hoped he didn't detect the nervous tremor in her voice. Because of the circumstances of their first encounter, and because of the autocratic appearance of the man, she felt strangely on edge and wished he would proceed to his table. She had not seen him at lunchtime and supposed that he had boarded the train at one of the infrequent stops.

'I shall escort you to your table.' He proceeded to do so, making instinctively for the table on which stood a bowl of small white orchids, the kind that grew wild and were known as Little White Nuns. 'I would invite you to dine at my table, *señorita*, but a friend will be joining me to discuss business. Perhaps afterwards you would take coffee with us in the club car?'

It was a request, and yet at the same time it was an order, and as Romy stood there, a cool contrast to his darkness, a small flame of defiance flared within her. 'I intend to have an early night, *señor*. Thank you all the same for the invitation.'

He met and held her eyes that were the cool green of mint, but instead of insisting he inclined his head and crossed the aisle to his own table, treading the floor of the swaying train with ease and assurance.

Romy sat down and turned her gaze to the window, and as the day darkened she felt the quickened beating of her heart. She hadn't dreamed that she would ever see the man again; had even parted from him in Mexico City with the hope that their paths would not cross in the future.

It had been hot that day, with a blazing warmth flooding down from the blue sky, intensifying the the earthy smells of the city and its teeming crowds. Romy had spent half the day in the cool halls of the museum of Aztec art, and on her way out the ground had suddenly heaved beneath her feet. Alarmed, she had clutched at the air and would have fallen down the steps if hands strong and sure had not saved her. 'It's an earth tremor! Quickly, out of the way of this tall building, all this glass!'

Confused, frightened, she had found herself sheltering with a stranger beneath the arch of a stone doorway. For several minutes the ground had pulsated and hot waves of heat had wafted up from the street pavements. Traffic had come to a standstill amidst the blare of motor-horns. People had run in various directions, seeking shelter and looking scared. Then gradually everything had gone still again, until the life of the city resumed its normal pace.

With a gasp of relief Romy had thanked her rescuer, who wore a suit of impeccable white and a shirt only a few shades darker than the tan of his face. He asked the name of her hotel and snapped his fingers for a cab. One drew into the kerb and he handed her into it . . . and followed her. On the journey through the streets that no longer pulsed with these strange waves of energy he talked about the Aztec arts, and all the while there was a look in his bronze eyes that said it wasn't wise, or circumspect, for a single young woman to be roaming a foreign city on her own.

It was the desk clerk at the hotel who told her the man's imposing name, and that he held a high position in the diplomatic service. He had also been famous in his youth as a daring *espada*.

Now in his middle thirties, the Don had lost

11

none of his matador grace and danger, and because he had such an odd effect upon her nerves Romy smiled with extra charm at the young waiter who came to her table. She ordered a roast leg of chicken, creamed potatoes, and long beans. He had a little English, so it wasn't difficult to make conversation with him.

'The *señorita* likes the flowers?' he asked shyly.

'They're lovely, perfect miniature orchids.' And she was aware as she spoke that Don Delgado glanced across the aisle, his black brows joined in a frown as she fondled the Little White Nuns. She felt again that tiny flare of antagonism as she defied the disapproving look in the Latin eyes.

'And does the *señorita* wish for a glass of wine with her meal?'

'Yes ... a glass of champagne would be very nice.'

'The *señorita* is celebrating?' The waiter had noticed the direction of her gaze as she ordered champagne and he cast a swift and curious glance at the distinguished figure of Don Delgado, who had now been joined by a soldier in a dashing uniform.

'Perhaps I am,' Romy smiled, for to be young, and on holiday, was something to celebrate.

She enjoyed her dinner, especially the peach waffles and cream, and at the end of it she slid past that table wreathed in good cigar smoke and hoped she was unnoticed. '*Vaya con Dios, señorita,*' murmured a deep voice, and at the same time she felt the flick of bronze eyes over her face.

'Goodnight, *señor*.' She hurried on her way and heard behind her a mutter of enquiry from the cavalry officer with whom Don Delgado dined. She had to admit that she admired the uniform. It was rather romantic that in this mechanised age, horse-soldiers should still patrol the vast grasslands of Mexico and the fawn-coloured deserts.

She closed the door of her compartment behind her and began to prepare for bed. Clad in her nightdress and robe, she stood at the mirror and brushed her long hair that curled slightly at the ends. It was Nonna who had persuaded her not to have her hair cut short, and Romy smiled a little as she reflected on the amusing facts and fancies of he grandmother's girlhood in a country vicarage. Nonna had once told her that there was something a bit diabolical about a very attractive man and that if she ever met one, and the moon was full and shining, she was to cover her eyes and drop a curtsey to the moon.

'How will that protect me?' Romy remembered how she had laughed, and how she had thought to herself that she was safe with Lance, that she knew him too well to be hurt by him.

'Who's talking about being protected?' Nonna had said in that dry way of hers. 'It's luck you'll be needing if you ever meet a devil of a man.'

Romy turned away from the mirror and pulled aside the curtain that covered the window near her bed, which the porter had made up while she was at dinner. What she saw from the window made her catch her breath in surprise; a torrent of rain had followed that wild-gold sunset and the wheels of the train had drowned the tumult. It fell in a solid sheet and Romy could hear the wind whistling past the train, racing it through the dark night.

She gave a little shiver and quickly closed the curtain. She swore to herself that she had not been looking for the moon, but when she opened a magazine before settling down for the night it was not a model arrayed in the latest fashion which she saw but a dark-browed autocrat who disapproved of self-reliant women.

It was disturbing that they should meet again. After that encounter during the earth tremor she had carefully avoided the Aztec museum and the Diplomatic quarter where he might be run into again. Being of an independent nature Romy was far from keen on dominating men who had old-fashioned ideas about women travelling alone and seeing something of the world.

Chaperones had surely gone out with the whalebone corset, which like some awful chastity belt had kept women securely in their place ... no doubt the kitchen and the nuptial bedchamber!

Romy buried her nose in her magazine, and heard in the corridor the chatter of people on their way to bed. Beyond the train windows the clamour of the rainstorm had not diminished, in fact it seemed to have increased in fury, and once again that tiny shiver of alarm ran through her slender frame.

Mexico was certainly an unpredictable land, and her people seemed of a similar disposition; their smouldering warmth surely held its own changes from charm to danger. The train rushed on through the wild night, and Romy tried to ignore her nervous tension. In the morning she would have breakfast in her compartment and avoid seeing Don Delgado for the remainder of the journey.

She gave a little yawn and folded her magazine. She glanced at her travelling clock and slipped out of her robe. Time for bed and, she hoped, a dreamless night. She turned down her sheets and plumped her pillows, and then remembered that she must bolt her door. As it was a sleeping compartment there was only one entrance, and without bothering to slip her feet into her mules she padded across to the door and was about to slide the bolt when there was an abrupt tap upon the panels.

Romy was staring at the door when with equal abruptness it opened and she retreated as a masculine figure strode into her compartment.

'What are you doing?' The words broke in quick alarm from her lips. 'How dare you come in here!'

There was only one person on the train who was so outrageously confident and golden-skinned; only one person in the world who could make her feel so immediately unsure and immature.

'Get out this instant!' The words rang with a Victorian indignation she might laugh at later on, but right now she was shocked that Don Delgado should come marching into her private domain dressed in a dark silk robe and pyjamas. What did he take her for, because she travelled alone? Fury tingled through her from the roots of her tawny hair to the soles of her small bare feet.

He didn't say a word for at least a minute, and his expression was unreadable as he stood there with the overhead light shining on his black hair. Then he glanced around her compartment with a casual air, as if contrasting its sombre panelling with her pale youthful skin and her single silk garment.

She felt the hammering of her heart as those remarkable eyes of his missed not a detail of her appearance. They dwelt with a disturbing intensity upon her hair, a cloud of tawny gold about her shoulders, tendrils clustering about her temples and intensifying the clear green of her indignant eyes.

'What do you want, *señor*?' she demanded.

'From the look in your eyes, *señorita*, you have decided what I want, and as you are a headstrong young woman travelling entirely alone you might well have cause to look alarmed. In this country girls who go about alone are asking for the attentions of men.'

'Which doesn't say very much for Latin males,' she retorted. 'In my country women are free to go where they please, and they don't have to be afraid that every man will accost them.'

'Perhaps that is because your countrymen play cricket on the village green instead of learning the art of bullfighting.' Small fiendish lights played in the Don's eyes. 'A Latin is taught from a boy that once he can master a bull, and then a woman, he is indeed a man.'

'I'm quite certain, Don Delgado, that female independence is to you like the flickering cape to the bull. Well, I am one woman who doesn't intend to be tamed by you, so please leave my compartment before I ring for the porter. I am sure your Latin sense of honour would hate a scandal.'

'It would be appalled.' A smile flickered on the firm, yet well moulded lips. 'You amuse me, *señorita*. You travel so audaciously alone in a strange country, yet a man has only to make the mistake of entering the wrong compartment and you are ready to cry wolf. A Latin girl with a *duenna* would have no need to be so afraid.'

'Are you suggesting that I get myself a *duenna*?' It was Romy's turn to smile scornfully. 'Chaperones went out with the bustle and the boa in my country.'

'But you are not in your country at the present moment.' His voice was as deliberate as his gaze. 'You are in Mexico.'

'I am well aware of that.' Her eyes flicked his lordly face, and she felt a panicky urge to snatch up her robe. Never before in her life had a man so disconcerted her, and she wanted to hide herself from those worldly Latin eyes with their deep glimmers of mockery. 'As it happens, *señor*, I prefer my own company and I would be grateful if you would bow out and leave me alone.'

'I embarrass you, eh?'

'Is it so surprising, *señor*? What if I screamed and aroused the other passengers?'

'You are not the type ... you are much too reserved to give way to hysterics at the sight of a mere man.' He spread his hands in a very Latin way and his hint of a smile revealed that he knew all about women and their reactions. He turned to the door. 'I will say once more *vaya con Dios* and leave you to your own company, which you so much prefer.'

'Don't you mean *vaya con diablo*?' she murmured irresistibly.

He swung her a look as his hand touched the door-handle. 'Travel with the devil, eh? Is that how you regard me?'

Her silence was her answer, and during that endless pause a heavy gust of wind launched itself at the windows and walls of the train, and a rumble of thunder seemed to fill the air. Romy pulled her gaze from the Don's and cast a nervous look at the rattling windows. She could not repress a shiver, and was unsure which unnerved her the most, the torrential rain outside, or the man who had invaded her privacy.

'Are you afraid of storms?' he asked. 'Are the rains and the wind less tempestuous in England?'

'Our climate is a bit more moderate.' Her green

eyes dwelt on his face with a flash of curiosity. 'You speak such perfect English that I believed you had been there.'

'One day I shall go there. I am intrigued by a country which allows its young women such a dangerous amount of freedom. Perhaps you come to Mexico because you are intrigued by the more restrictive ideas with regard to women?'

'Mexico is colourful and historical, Don Delgado. Women in seclusion, guarded by elderly *duennas*, have all my sympathy.'

'You would doubtless have theirs, so young and alone, and at the mercy of strangers. To them it would seem that you had no one at home who loved you and cared what became of you.'

There wasn't anyone who really cared what became of her, but she wasn't going to admit such a painful truth to this man. It really was none of his business.

'In England girls are reared to stand firmly on their own two feet ...' The words had hardly left her lips when Romy was thrown off her feet ... the train gave a frightening lurch, its wheels screeched on the tracks, and then it rocked as if giant hands had taken hold of it. Romy gave a strangled cry as hands caught hold of her and dragged her close to a hard chest. Everything slid, fell, shattered ... it was as if the destruction of the train was imminent, and as the lights blinked and faded, the sense of doom was horribly intensified.

'Oh ... heavens!' Romy clung to her only support in a reeling world, this stranger who in another place, upon a similar occasion, had offered the shelter of his arms as the earth rocked.

CHAPTER TWO

THE train had run into some obstacle and by a miracle had not piled up, one carriage upon another. It had tilted and flung people willy-nilly.

Romy and the Don had been flung upon her bed, to become muffled in the covers and the folds of her silk robe. When the lights struggled on again Romy felt a sense of fear not entirely connected with the mishap to the train.

'Eyes of the Madonna!' She was held to the bed as Don Delgado raised himself and gazed down at her in the dim light. Her eyes were wide and densely green in her white face. Her nightdress was half off her shoulder, and every nerve in her shaken body was aware of the closeness of him. She was close to panic in his arms, and then to her acute relief he released her and slid off the bed. His black hair was slicked back with an impatient hand as he planted his feet wide and braced himself against the slope of the floor.

'My theory about you is proved, *señorita*, you are not the screaming sort.' Those fiendish little glints were alive in his eyes again. 'There has no doubt been a landslide on the railway lines and by a miracle not a headlong crash. However, the situation is obviously a grim one, so if you are now feeling a trifle less shaken I will go and ensure that not too many people are injured.'

'I ... I feel all right, *señor*. Yes, please go and assist ...'

He bowed ironically and made his way to the door. He took hold of the handle and pulled. He shook it, pushed and coaxed, and thrust a shoulder hard against the door. When after several minutes it refused to yield, he cursed softly in Spanish. 'The door has jammed! The angle at which the train has come to a halt has dislodged the mechanism and we are firmly locked in.'

'Oh no!' Romy knelt on the bed—as if in supplication—and watched in alarm as Don Delgado fought to open the imprisoning door. 'I have a nail file ... will that help, *señor*?'

'I need a crowbar.' He swung round to face her and his teeth showed themselves in a smile of grim humour. 'I suppose you don't happen to have one beneath your pillow?'

'Hardly.' She could feel her heart hammering from the double shock of the crash and the closure. 'D-don't you carry one of those knives with all the gadgets attached?'

'I am not exactly a schoolboy, which fact you have doubtless noticed, and if I carried a knife it would not be in the pocket of my dressing-gown.' He swept his sardonic eyes over her kneeling figure. 'I fear you are going to need all your British courage. We are without doubt locked together in your compartment and there is no way of knowing when we will be released. Those in charge of the train will attend first to those who have been hurt, and it may take until daylight for all sections of the train to be checked.'

'Daylight?' Her slim body went tense with shock. 'You can't mean that we have to stay together ... all night?'

'I have no axe.' His teeth seemed to bite out the words. 'No iron bar with which to break open the door.'

'Are you quite sure that it won't open.' She looked at him almost accusingly. 'Please do something, Don Delgado!'

'What do you suggest?' He quirked a sable eyebrow and seemed to enjoy the predicament in which they were placed. 'That I pray the ground might open so I can return to the nether regions? You may blame me for walking into your compartment by mistake, but don't look at me as if I arranged for the train to run off the rails.'

'There's no need to be sarcastic.' Her eyes flashed. 'I realise the gravity of the derailment, but I refuse to believe that we are trapped here until the morning. If we bang on the window or yell out someone is bound to hear us and fetch help.'

'If you will just listen a moment, *señorita*, you will hear there are people in other carriages calling for help. We are fortunate not to have been injured.'

'But a rescue squad will surely arrive before morning?'

'Perhaps.' He shrugged his shoulders and leaned against the door that had somehow locked them in. 'I would point out, however, that we are in the wilds of Mexico. and I predict that it will be some time before aid arrives for even the injured. There is in the nature of the Latin a tendency towards fatalism. That what is to be, will be. Destiny. The hand of chance. Taking hold of this train in the stormy night and stranding its passengers in the middle of nowhere. Listen to the wind ... it cries above the voices like a banshee.'

Yes, it mingled with the cries of distress and made everything seem like an awful dream ... yet no face in a dream of Romy's had ever looked so alive and forceful as Don Delgado's, as he stood there looking at her, his wide, silk-clad shoulders against the door that imprisoned them. 'A country as vast as Mexico,' he said, 'still retains many of the old beliefs. In many ways it must seem strange to an English girl, whose parents were very unwise to allow her to travel through this country as if its deserts, its volcanoes, its extremes of climate did not exist. Did they think it a soft, green land? Did they believe its people tame? Did they not realise that in an unpredictable country anything might happen to a young woman unescorted?'

Romy huddled on the bed like a small girl, and though she could hear the clamour of the other passengers on the stricken train, it was only Don Delgado of whom she was utterly aware. She could feel herself trembling, and she knew that most of it was caused by the man who calmly informed her that she must spend the night with him.

It was the first time in her life that she had been so intimately alone with a man, and there was nowhere she could run to escape him. His darkness, his lean matador grace, his powerful personality ... they combined to make her acutely aware of her own youth and innocence. He made Lance seem like an unfledged boy!

'I can take care of myself.' She spoke with a bravado she did not feel. 'I have been doing so, oh, for years. This trip is my first real holiday. I work for my living; I'm not a pampered socialite.'

'I never supposed you were, *señorita*. You are far too amiable towards young waiters, far too eager a tourist, far too interested in the Indians and their history to be a globe-trotting sophisticate.' With a lean, expressive hand he took a slim leather case from his pocket. 'You permit that I smoke?'

'Do you need to ask, *señor*?'

'But of course. There are women who object to the smoking habit.'

'But do you take heed of any woman's objection?'

'If it pleases me to do so, otherwise no.' He took a thin cigar from the case, and his seal ring of heavy gold caught the dull light and revealed itself as a heavily carved family ring, probably dating back to the days of the Conquest. As his lighter flared and he projected smoke from his nostrils, his face was stamped with a Latin autocracy. There was not a tinge of copper in his skin. He was a descendant of a line which had never intermarried; their cream-skinned brides chosen from the Iberian convents in Spain, where girls of good family were kept in seclusion until the time was ripe for the arranged marriage to take place. Then the girl, in the close company of her *duenna,* would travel to Mexico to be married in one of the golden churches to a man she had never met before. It was a romantically barbaric custom, the giving of a girl to a stranger who might be cruel or indifferent.

Aware that she was staring, and yet unable to drag her eyes away from the Don's face, Romy felt all these thoughts racing through her mind. Don Delgado de Avarado y Valcazar was like tempered steel that might be cruel, and there slumbered in his eyes a fire that might frighten a girl.

The fine smoke of his cigar tendrilled its way to the ceiling, and he watched it lazily.

'We are bound by circumstances to spend tonight in each other's company,' he said, 'so I suggest you relax and try to stop regarding me in the manner of a white mouse which expects at any moment to be attacked by a large and rather wicked cat. Please to put on your robe—I can see you are trembling—and we will attempt to make the best of the situation.'

'Do you really think it will be hours before some-one ... *señor,* what about your friend the cavalry officer? Won't he look for you?'

'If I know Javier he will be helping those in real need. He is a dedicated soldier, and he will assume that I am busy doing my share to help the unfortunate. I only wish I could be of use, but fate has decreed otherwise.'

'I didn't ask you to come blundering in through my door.' Romy tied the sash of her robe in a tight knot. 'It isn't my fault that you're here. I was all ready to go to bed and was about to bolt my door for the night.'

'Now destiny has bolted it,' he drawled, 'and you have company, whether you wish it or not. Have you a pack of playing cards in your overnight bag?'

'Yes.' She gazed at him wide-eyed. 'I like to play solitaire.'

'A game for the lonely. Are you a lonely person, *señorita*?'

'I have no *duenna, señor*,' she said demurely.

His smile was a brief flash of strong teeth against the skin that was like golden leather. 'May I have the cards?'

'Of course.' She reached for her bag, then noticed that with her toilet articles it had been flung to the floor when the train came to its precipitous halt and the contents had spilled out. Don Delgado, who seemed to possess a catlike sense of balance, stepped across to the bag and one by one he picked up her scattered belongings and gave each an amused glance. Pretty trifles that looked lost in his hand, like her lacy handkerchief and a tiny ivory charm, which he studied for a minute, his cigar clenched in his teeth, his eyelids lowered against the smoke.

'You are superstitious?' he asked.

'I suppose most people are, *señor*. You seem yourself to believe that fate takes a hand in most things that happen.'

'I am a Latin and so I have my beliefs in the machinations of fate.' As he spoke he studied the snapshot which had fallen from her wallet, then he glanced at her with a sudden intensity. 'This is your brother?'

'No.' Her heart gave a thump beneath the silk of her robe, which was a soft rose colour and not unbecoming. 'I have no brothers.'

'A cousin, perhaps?'

'My only cousin is a girl.'

'I see.' He dropped the snapshot into her bag, snapped it shut, and handed it to her. 'I think everything is safe, including your passport and papers ... this tiny gun I shall keep in my pocket for the time being. It is a pretty-looking toy, but dangerous in the nervous hands of a girl in company she does not seem to care for.' His smile was diabolical. 'Now with your permission, or without it, Miss Ellyn, I will take a seat on the foot of your bed and we will play a game of cards.'

Romy watched, with a certain feeling of helplessness, as the lean hands dealt the cards. The Don's face in the dim light had a fascination she could not deny, but he was right when he said she was uneasy in his company. He had walked in here at at fateful moment, and whether she liked him or not, she had to endure him until daylight came. Her only consoling thought was that when the morning came and he was released from her compartment she need never see him again.

She picked up her cards and fanned them ... the king of diamonds stared at her and for some odd reason she thought of the Don's first name. Delgado in Spanish meant light, but his hair was so very dark, and his brows and lashes cast shadows on the autocratic planes of his face.

Light ... Lucifer ... dark angel.

'Please to begin, Miss Ellyn.'

She didn't bother to ask how he knew her surname; his keen eyes would have noticed the name on her passport. Almost deliberately she tossed away the king that she held.

'That is a dangerous card to treat so carelessly.' Romy felt the flick of the Don's eyes. 'Do you want to lose to me?'

'We are only playing to pass the time,' she retorted.

'And you can't wait for daylight to come fast enough, eh?'

'I shan't be ... sorry.'

'I hope indeed that you won't be ... sorry.' His glance took in the tawny hair clouding about her young face, and a sardonic smile edged his lips. Beyond the fast closed door of the compartment a good deal of shouting activity was still in progress ... Romy and the Don were part of it, and yet curiously apart from it. They were a pair of hostile strangers, forced to spend an entire night together.

As their game proceeded Romy was intensely aware of the dark figure at the foot of her bed, watching her from beneath those rather heavy eyelids, everything about him so forceful and male and mockingly aware that he made her feel about as composed as a moth on a pin. Whatever would Iris and her aunt have to say if they could see her now ... what would Lance have said, if he had really cared for her?

This is real, Romy thought wildly. I really am trapped in the compartment of a train with a man who looks as if he has always had his own way. Suppose he reached out and dragged her into those strong arms ... if she screamed no one would take much notice, they would think her just another hysterical passenger.

'What an expressive face you have,' drawled the Don. 'Right now you are wondering what you will do if I become amorous. It might be amusing to find out ... please, *señorita*, don't jump out of your pretty English skin. When you do that you really give yourself away as a total innocent. And I think a rare puritan. It really was astute of that young waiter in the dining-car to put White Nun orchids on your table.'

Don Delgado studied Romy, and there was a mocking kind of gravity in his eyes that made her want to throw the word Devil in his face. She tensed herself for a sudden move from him, and she very nearly did scream when he did move his hand, to the pocket of his dressing-gown for his cigar case.

'I shall smoke,' he drawled, 'just to soothe your nerves.'

'My nerves are perfectly all right,' she rejoined. 'But it isn't every night of my life that I'm involved in a train disaster, forced to spend hours with a stranger, and subject to his sarcasm because I happen to have English ways instead of those of a Latin girl. It must be nerve-racking for you, Don Delgado, to have to spend the night with someone you obviously despise.'

He regarded her through the smoke of his cigar and that ironic little smile tugged at his lips. 'You leap to conclusions that are not justified, *señorita*. Latin girls are a lot more cautious, but in a crisis they are often less than calm. You did not scream when the train ran into trouble, yet you almost did so when I reached for my cigar case. Tell me, do you take me for a libertine?'

'If I am as naïve and innocent as you think me, *señor*, then I am bound to be suspicious of you.'

'Why me in particular?'

Her eyes were fastened upon his face and all that she had to fear was surely written there. He was far too striking and subtle not to be a man who could—when he wished—bend any woman to his will. She closed her eyes in order to shut out that handsome and dangerous face, and it was only a few seconds later that her tired young head drooped on the pillow and the playing cards fell from her hand. She went quietly to sleep, the tang of cigar smoke drifting to her nostrils, unaware of the moment when the Don arose and wrapped the coverlet about her. In her sleep she murmured something and he bent his dark head in order to catch the words. When he straightened up he was frowning slightly and his heavy-lidded gaze dwelt on the handbag whose contents he had picked up from the floor of the compartment, whose privacy he had also invaded.

Romy was fast asleep when a hand touched her shoulder and aroused her. She opened her eyes and lay a moment, confused by her surroundings and by the rather stern face that met her gaze in the dawn light. The events of last night began to filter back to her mind and her emotions, and before she could stop herself she shrank away from the touch of Don Delgado's hand.

'Ambulances are here.' His black brows joined in a level line above his bronze eyes. 'Before long men will start to check on the occupants of these compartments. Miss Ellyn, we must talk!'

She struggled into a sitting position. 'What more is there to talk about, señor? Look, it's morning ... soon the men will have the door open!'

'Almost too soon, and there is something I must say to you which I have saved for this last half hour we will be alone.'

Her eyes dwelt on him, wide and hazily green from sleep. She watched as he took a seat on the side of the bed, and the thought struck her again that in his personal relationships with women he must be overwhelming. For the first time she wondered if he was a married man ... if so how would he explain last night's escapade if it reached his wife's ears?

'I am glad that you managed to get some sleep.' As he spoke he was studying the heavy gold ring he wore and the seal carved upon it. 'You have doubtless heard that we of Latin blood have strong feelings of honour?' he said, somewhat drily. 'If that does not sound too old-fashioned to a modern-minded English girl?'

'I have heard something of the sort, *señor*.'

'Well, it happens to be a fact,' he crisped, 'and the night we have just spent together places both of us in a situation of the most awkward ... I should not care to be labelled shameless, would you?'

'Shameless ... ?' Romy forced herself to meet the Don's eyes and their expression caused her heart to give a thump. 'But we did ... nothing. We played cards and you told me about your country. We have only to tell the truth ...'

'This is one of those occasions when the truth, I fear, would sound like a tale we had manufactured in an attempt to save our faces.' The ring on his hand gleamed almost malevolently as he indicated his dressing-gown and dark silk pyjamas. 'Because I am clad like this it will be assumed that I came to your compartment with the intention of staying the night, or part of it. Then when the train ran into misfortune I found myself forced to remain here because the door had jammed. All very logical, and damning.'

'But you are a Consul,' Romy protested. 'Your word is surely your bond?'

'In Latin eyes, *señorita*, a man is judged first and foremost as a man.' A grim little smile played about his lips as he scanned her face and saw its increasing alarm. 'It really was indiscreet of you to travel alone in my country. Such an invitation to trouble would not be presented by a Latin girl; those of good family travel always with a companion and if last night's mishap had occurred in front of a witness, neither of us would be in jeopardy.'

'I . . . I don't care if I am taken for a liar,' Romy said defiantly. 'Your people can believe what they like. *I* know the truth and that's all I care about.'

'It may be all you care about, Miss Ellyn, but my code is not quite so elastic.'

'If your Latin rules are so rigid, then why do Latin girls have to be chaperoned as if they aren't to be trusted? It would seem, *señor*, that you people are all too ready to believe that men and women aren't to be trusted on their own. Well, I'm English and I don't make eyes at men over a lace fan, or invite their attentions because I have the safeguard of a *duenna*.'

'Tell me, *señorita*,' he leaned forward and his gaze was so sardonic as to be downright devilish, 'if we were in your country, right now, and the situation was the same, that we were locked together in a railway compartment, would it really be believed that I spent last night at the foot of your bed?'

'I don't see why not!' She spoke with a bravado she didn't really feel, not with those sardonic eyes mocking her, and informing her that not everyone had her own innocent sort of mind. 'In any case, it would be shrugged off, not treated like a point of honour which must be remedied at all cost. I am sure, Don Delgado, that you have not lived such a blameless life that one so-called indiscretion will be held against you.'

'A man's indiscretions, Miss Ellyn, are not usually on display as this one will be when that door is forced open and I am discovered here with you ... to all intents and purposes your lover!'

'My lover?' she gasped, and her green eyes were shocked as they raced over his face, which in the struggling morning light was made even more sardonic by his unshaven chin, and by the overnight disarray of his usually well-groomed hair.

'Perhaps you had better break my neck, *señor*, and call me a victim of the crash.'

'*Qué brava*, are you not?'

'I try to be.' She thrust up her chin even as her hand crept to the neck of her robe and clasped it to hide her white skin and the pulse that throbbed there so nervously.

'And you like it that people admire your British courage?' His eyes had narrowed in a rather dangerous way, as if each small action of hers was aimed against that infernal honour of his.

'Yes, I like it.' She was finding also that she enjoyed defying this Spanish autocrat. 'I suppose you prefer girls who submit to your will without even a struggle?'

'It does save the energy for better things,' he drawled, and tiny fires were flickering behind those dense black lashes that surrounded his unusual eyes. 'A Spaniard likes to be held in high esteem, Miss Ellyn. He has a deep, inborn sense of decorum, as instinctive as the proven courage of the British. He finds that his conscience is not easy to live with if he fails to fulfil a duty.'

'I have read *Don Quixote*,' she murmured. 'Surely you aren't saying that a Spaniard would go to such extremes to prove himself honourable?'

'He would go beyond them, Miss Ellyn, and he has often done so. Each of us is a relic of the past, of ancestors who made us. Your hair and your eyes are a living proof that you have a Celtic heritage. Mine is linked to the Knights of Santiago, and the wars against the infidels.'

'You mean,' her green eyes blazed, 'that your ancestors burned at the stake those who rebelled against their laws!'

'Perhaps.' He shrugged. 'You with your green eyes might be descended from a sorceress. Who knows? The only certainty is that in a very short while we are going to be found together in a most compromising way.'

'Then we must shrug it off,' she said. 'Just as you have just shrugged off those poor devils your ancestors burned.'

'Sweet breath of life,' he said with dangerous softness. 'Are you quite such a child that you don't see the consequences of last night and being so alone with a man of my age, my position, my blood? Look at you! It would take a saint to believe that we played card games throughout the night.' He said it bluntly, almost brutally, and brought wild colour storming into her cheeks. 'Miss Ellyn, you are altogether too tempting a young person for the truth to be believable. You give the eyes a little too much pleasure!'

'Am I supposed to be bowled over by the compliment?' Her cheeks burned as his eyes swept over her. 'I thought you looked a devil in Mexico City, now I know you are.'

'Not such a devil, *señorita*, that I took advantage of your ineffable innocence and made of you what people will call you ... if I don't redeem your good name by telling everyone you are the young woman I am going to marry.'

CHAPTER THREE

'*Marry you* ...?'

It was as if a thunderclap shook the train, but in reality it was the railway engineers shunting the train back on the lines. It shuddered a moment and then steadied, and Romy had a curious sensation

36

of giddiness.

She stared at Don Delgado in a dazed way. 'You tell me I must become engaged to you, just like that! People in my country fall in love before taking such a step.'

'There is little time left for falling in love.' His tone of voice held the essence of irony. 'The train has been righted and any minute now that door will be forced open and we will be found together ... in a mutual state of undress!'

'I ... I must dress!' Romy looked desperate ... the compartment was filling with daylight and she could hear deep voices in the corridor, those of the rescue workers.

'Where will you dress?' The Don asked the question with a wicked courtesy. 'In front of me?'

Romy caught her breath and realised in an instant that it was far more intimate for a woman to dress in front of a man than to be lightly clad in his presence. She seemed to burn from head to toe as the Latin eyes dwelt on her with a worldly awareness of her innocence.

'Now do you begin to see how things are? We are male and female, and our every action, imprisoned as we are, is made a thing of guilt. The only way we overcome the guilt is to be a man with his prospective bride when that door is opened.'

'Y-you can't be serious?' Romy wanted to be scornful, but his expression warned her that he was not joking. 'You are *serious* about all this? You mean what you are saying?'

'Every word, Miss Ellyn.'

'But it's so drastic. How can I pretend to care for you ... to have a feeling of affection for someone I hardly know?'

'Affection?' he queried. 'What a very tame word.'

'It's a better word than blackmail!'

'Blackmail, Miss Ellyn? What I am suggesting is a betrothal in place of a scandal. Surely your family would be most affronted if they heard you had been disgraced by a Spaniard in the wilds of Mexico?'

'I have no family.'

'So!' He slowly raised an eyebrow. 'Now I understand why you please yourself and take little heed of your safety in a strange land. Why would you not tell me before that you had no parents? Did you really believe that I would take advantage of you?'

'Aren't you taking advantage when you suggest that I become your fiancée? How do I know that you will set me free afterwards, to go my own way? For all I know an engagement in Mexico may be as binding as a marriage, and you are the last man on earth I should wish to marry.'

'*Gracias.*' He stood up and gave her an ironical bow. 'What a pity we have no witness to prove our mutual antipathy, but as things are no one will believe that such angelic lips can be so unkind.'

'Do you really care what other people believe?'

'As Consul to this part of the country I have to care. An adventure with a woman is all very well, but not on my own doorstep. A pity for both of us, but I refuse to dishonour my own prestige.'

'You speak like a man who places pride before anything else,' she accused. 'I am sure my feelings are of little account to you.'

'On the contrary, I am making amends for my blunder of last night, when I mistook this compartment for that of my friend. Surely you would prefer to be thought my fiancée than a girl of light morals, the English girl who spent a night of love with a Spaniard on a train.'

'There was no night of love!' she gasped.

'In the eyes of everyone else it will seem so. What a drama they will make of it, with railway victims in other carriages, and the train half derailed. Two people who snatched at romance during a train wreck.'

'The train has not been wrecked!'

'Our reputations will surely be wrecked if you refuse to listen to good sense.' His voice roughened and abruptly he reached for her hand, which was plucking restlessly at the bedcover. 'I do assure you that my *hacienda* in the Valle del Sol is quite lovely, for all its age. It should appeal greatly to your vivid imagination.'

'You present your valley home like a bribe, *señor*. A toy to make a sulky child behave herself and obey.'

'I can see that compliance to a man's dictates does not come easily to you, and that tells me something very significant.'

'Really?' She tried to free her hand from his, but

his grip was like a vice, strong and on the edge of being painful. 'Won't you tell me what is so significant and not keep the secret to yourself? Oh, you're hurting my wrist!'

'I think before you are much older, *chica*, I shall spank you. Latin girls are taught to have some respect for the man they are to marry.'

'You are not that man!' she broke in. But even as she spoke her qualms of unease were growing stronger. His powerful fingers were holding her hand and the contact made her feel as defenceless as the child he called her. She was alone in a strange land whose codes were far more rigid and unforgiving than those of England. She knew just by looking at the Don's proud face that he belonged to one of the notable families of the region; people interwoven into the history of the country, to whom scandal would be like poison.

'Let us understand one another,' he said crisply. 'This engagement will take place because circumstances decree that it should. But we are not forced to love one another ... though you have a certain *buen angel* charm which is your own downfall, and mine. If you lacked such charm I could walk away from you ... as it is I must protect you.'

'And do you expect a demure acceptance of such a great honour?' Her green eyes were defiant, and yet a shade of terror lurked in them. 'Do you really think I'll be sacrificed to save your blushes?'

'It is your blushes I am saving, Miss Ellyn. Last night at dinner you were given White Nun orchids.

Would you prefer scarlet roses for a scarlet woman?'

'Y-you have a cruel way of putting things, Don Delgado.'

'I am sorry if I am cruel in what I say, but we Latins are a realistic race of people. We have also a saying: resist Fate and darken your own eye. Is it not much nicer, when all is said and done, to be held in esteem by other people? You fondled the small white flowers the young man gave you ... to-night a young man might ask you for some of those kisses you are reputed to give so freely.'

'Don't ... please.' She was startled by her own degree of shock ... men were cruel in that way, if they thought a girl an easy target, and even with Lance she had been shy of being kissed. Perhaps she was idealistic, but something within her wanted a man's kisses to be associated with a fond love. Perhaps instinctively she had always known that Lance was rather shallow ... and to be thought shallow herself was something she could hardly endure.

'It's true,' she murmured. 'I have to bow down to your wishes ... oh, but I can't! We're almost strangers. You are a Spaniard, with ways and customs so different from my own!'

'It will at first be bewildering for you, but we have no choice ... do you hear? They are battering the door!'

And as the flames of a new day lit the sky and stabbed into the compartment, the lock of the door was forced to yield, and a workman and a railway official were standing there in the aperture, taking in with curious eyes the girl in the bed, and the dark personage who towered at the side of it, hands thrust into the pockets of his heavy silk dressing-gown.

'Don Delgado!' exclaimed the official.

The Don inclined his dark head as if they had just met politely on the street. '*Buenos dias*, Inspector. I hope there is not too much trouble with the line, and no one seriously injured?'

Though he spoke in Spanish, Romy knew from the calm tone of his voice that he was determined not to seem embarassed. The Mexican workman was staring at her, and instantly the Don snapped out an order that made the man retreat from the compartment. Her cheeks flamed. She felt instantly the force of Spanish protectiveness ... the Don had decided her fate, and though she hardly understood his language she could sense the meaning of his words.

'The young lady is my betrothed. We are on our way to my *hacienda* to announce that we will be married in the family chapel. I came last night to wish my *novia* goodnight, then the crash occurred and the door became jammed.'

The words were spoken, the fatal announcement was made, and Romy's hand slowly clenched the sheet as consternation cleared from the Inspector's face. 'Everything is understood, Excellency. And everyone will be most happy for you.'

'*Gracias*.' Don Delgado did not glance at Romy, and for about five minutes more he and the official talked rapidly together, no doubt about the trouble on the line. Then she caught the Spanish word for breakfast, which she knew, and a moment later, with a polite and smiling bow the Inspector withdrew and closed as far as possible the shattered door.

Then the Don turned slowly to gaze at Romy. 'It is done,' he said, speaking now in his impeccable English, with that accent which stressed certain words in a rather disturbing way. 'You are now my bride-to-be, and not a soul will dare to breathe a word against you. Come, try to smile. The Valle del Sol is not the nether regions!'

Because he was so adept at reading her mind, the panic went racing through her veins and she hardly dared to look at the man who was claiming the right to call her his intended bride. Heavens, how would she feel if they were not pretending?

'I should like to know your first name,' he said. 'I noticed your surname on your passport.'

She swallowed dryly. 'I was christened Romola, but when I was almost three years old I was left parentless and relatives took charge of me. My grandmother always called me Romy, and I rather like it.'

'Yet Romola has something Latin about it.' Then at the glance she gave him a sardonic gleam sprang into his eyes. 'Don't be afraid, I shall not try to make of you a Spanish girl. I prefer originals to copies, and there is much that is original about you.'

'Is there . . . all I know right now, *señor*, is that my

mind is in a turmoil and I'm rather afraid of you ...'

'Come, *niña*, you kept your head most admirably last night, and there is no reason to think you will lose it in the future. We are only playing a game, so try not to look such a reluctant fiancée.'

'Were many people hurt last night?' she asked.

'About a dozen, but not seriously. The driver of the train was admirably quick in sighting a fall of rock on the lines. The heavy rains had brought it down. Engineers are now busy repairing the damage caused by the derailment, and I am told that passengers will be disembarked after breakfast to await transport to take them on to Xerica.'

'I am bound for Xerica,' she said eagerly.

'You were bound for that particular place, but not now.' He spoke decisively. 'I have ordered breakfast to be brought to you, then you will dress and we will leave the train together. My *hacienda* is about ten miles from here—I should in the normal course of events have left the train at the next station—and I shall try to arrange some means of transport for us.'

'You are very determined, *señor*, once your mind is made up.' She smiled with a certain wistfulness. 'I feel rather like a twig bouncing on a tempestuous stream. Do we have to go through with your drastic proposal? Can't we say that we had a fearful tiff and called off the ... marriage?'

'If I were not the Consul of half this territory, then a lovers' tiff might be easier to arrange. *Por cierto*, for both of us this is a serious matter. You saw the way those men looked at you! Did you enjoy the feeling?'

She gave a little shudder. In Mexico City she had known from the air about this man that he was someone notable. On board this train he was Excellency ... he could not be seen to have spent a night with a young, single English girl and not be talked about. Her own notoriety would precede her to Xerica, and to Vera Cruz, and already she had found that Mexican men were bolder in their approaches than Englishmen. She would in their eyes be the scarlet woman of the Don's graphic description.

'You must accept the turn of events,' he said. 'The rainstorm, the wrecking, and soon the haven of my *hacienda*.'

'The Valley of the Sun,' she murmured. 'It sounds like a place of Aztec worship.'

'Long ago the valley did belong to the Aztec people, and the *hacienda* is built upon the site of one of their pagan temples.' His hands moved expressively. 'Strange that our first meeting should take place outside the museum where you were studying their customs. Do you remember? You had made sketches and you showed me some of them as we drove in a cab to your hotel.'

'Yes, I remember.' How could she ever forget? His face and his voice had lingered in her memory for days afterwards. She told herself it was because they had met at a dangerous moment, while the earth shook and the many windows of the tall cubic building shimmered in the hot sunlight.

How could she have known they would meet again ... that here in the very wilds of Mexico she would be thrown upon his mercy, a victim of his pride and the prejudices of this unknown land.

'So after breakfast I prepare myself to go with you ... to the Valley of the Sun, *señor*?'

'Yes, *niña*.' His eyes held hers and the smile that edged his lips added to the subtlety of his face. 'Please try to look as if the prospect appeals to you, and not as if the Devil himself proposed to take you to his domain. The valley is an evocative place, and I have the strong impression that your relatives in England are not exactly congenial. Why do you brood ... because of the young man in the photograph holding aloft a tennis racket?'

Words clamoured through Romy. She wanted to deny the lack of affection in her aunt's home, and was wildly tempted to say that she loved him and *must* return to him. Then she saw the adamantine set to the Spanish jaw, the glinting of the bronze eyes, and that strange new fear of another person held her in its grip, numbing the words that sprang to her lips. She had loved Lance, in a girlish, idealistic way, but now he was the husband of her cousin, and gone forever was that feeling of youthful worship. She knew now that he had just been pleasant to be with as a playmate. Good at tennis, swimming, and horseback riding. Charming and gay, and popular with everyone. She hated to admit what her heart knew, that he had married Iris so he could run his own riding school. Romy could not have given him that.

'Lance was just a friend,' she said.

'He must have been close to you, if you carry his likeness?'

'We knew each other from children. He had no sisters so he taught me how to swim and ride.'

'Ah, you can ride! Excellent. We have horses at the *hacienda* and I like them to get as much exercise as possible. Their strain is Arabian and you will enjoy their swiftness. You see,' his eyes were mocking, but also fleetingly indulgent, 'I shall not be altogether the tyrant.'

'I should hope not,' she said, with a flash of spirit. 'I am going with you for your sake as much as for my own.'

'Do you know what name the Spanish give to our type of engagement, *señorita*?'

'Something pretty strong, I imagine.'

'They call it Iberian rape.' He quirked an eyebrow. 'Which means that everyone believes we have eloped and made love before taking the marriage vows. A very dramatic thing to do in Latin eyes, and hard to live down if the man fails to offer his name to the girl.'

'What if the couple swore on oath that they had not ... made love?'

'Few Spanish men would risk their reputation as a *novillo*.'

'And what is that, *señor*?'

47

'A young bull.'

'I see.' Colour stung her cheeks. 'So in order to boost your prestige, that of the daring *espada* and the ardent lover, I must hand myself over to you and your family ... rather like a sacrifice on those temple stones your home is built upon.'

He considered her way of putting it, and then with a brief smile he inclined his head in agreement. 'Perhaps so, but I don't play this game of make-believe entirely from self-interest. I have my family's integrity to think of. Don't mistake me. Latin people are not narrow-minded. A man may have his affairs of the heart, but with an experienced woman, not a girl who is young enough to look seduced. My name would be mud among those who work for me, and a thing of scorn to those of notable family. Ah, they would say, has Don Delgado taken to seducing young visitors to our country? *Ay, Dios*, it would not be a pretty thing for members of my family to hear from the lips of their friends.'

Romy studied his proud face and realised that it would be anathema for him to be labelled a seducer. He would sooner sacrifice his personal happiness than have the clinging mud of gossip thrown at his imposing historic family name.

Never leave the highway for the byway, flashed through her mind. *There you might meet the Devil himself.*

At that precise moment, just as she was on the verge of crying out that she couldn't even pretend to be his fiancée, there came a tap upon the door. *'Espere un momento.'* The Don bent over Romy and took her hand. 'I know your thoughts, *señorita.* Your eyes reveal them all too clearly. Have courage and don't try to fight the unkind fate which has caused us to be trapped like this. You are not, remember, the only one who has to pretend to be in love.'

'I ... I couldn't possibly love you!' The words broke from her.

'But I hope you can eat the food I have ordered for you.' His face was unreadable as he carried her hand to his lips and kissed the slim cold fingers. The next moment he swung on his heel and left her, and the waiter who carried in her breakfast was the young man who had been so kind to her. This morning his eyes evaded a meeting with hers. He placed the tray on the table and poured out her coffee, then with a distant little bow he withdrew from the compartment.

Romy sugared her coffee and took a look at the food beneath the covered dishes. Eggs and crisp rashers of bacon, hot rolls and butter, and a jar of honey ... but no chaste white flowers for the *señorita.*

Romy ate the food quite hungrily, as if her body and nerves needed the nourishment in order to tackle the problems that lay ahead of her. She drank her coffee, and after fixing a chair against the door she washed and dressed herself in a leaf-green linen suit. Her shoes had slender high heels that added to her height and her dignity. The mirror reflected the gravity of her face framed by her hair in a soft madonna style. Her new clothes, bought with part of Nonna's legacy, gave her a certain elegance which she had lacked at Lovtanet Bay, where she had roamed about the shore and the moors in casual jeans and jumpers. She had been the young cousin who often felt unwanted in her aunt's household, and now as she looked back she guessed why Aunt Madge had been so snappy with her. She had set her cap at Lance for her own daughter, and with hard cash she had bought an attractive, easy-going son-in-law.

Romy gave a sigh. Growing up in this world meant learning about other people, and trying not to be hurt when they turned out not to be the godlike creatures you thought them. She missed Nonna. She had no one, now, to whom she could turn for a word of wisdom.

What would Nonna have said about Don Delgado? 'Aye, wickedly attractive, my girl. Watch out for that moon and turn your silver, for you're going to need all the luck you can muster.'

Romy felt that she was going to need all her courage as well. She gazed critically at her own reflection and saw a girl with wide, enquiring green eyes, and features that were alive and sensitive. Don Delgado had said that she gave pleasure to the eyes, therefore no one would believe that he was not her lover.

She saw terror darken her eyes at the bare

thought, and she wondered if she could possibly escape from the train and find some means of getting away from him. She glanced out of the window and saw a lot of activity going on. Vehicles were at the track side, and people were standing about in anxious groups. Some of them were holding children, others were eating a sandwich or wandering aimlessly about.

She could surely lose herself among all these people, and could afford to pay anyone with a car, or a van, to take her to Xerica. She snapped the locks of her suitcases and swept a last look around the compartment which still seemed to hold images she would sooner forget. She made for the door and pushed aside the chair that secured the broken lock. The door swung open ... to disclose in the corridor a suave figure clad in a white shirt, cavalry breeches, and knee-high riding boots with spurs at the heels.

'There you are!' The Don flicked his eyes over her stunned face. 'I have borrowed my friend's horse and we shall ride to the *hacienda*. Our luggage will be collected later ... come with me!'

'No ... please let me go on to Xerica!'

But her plea was something he chose not to hear, and in a stride he reached her side and took her by the arm, with fingers that felt like iron. 'Come, we must be on our way.'

She wanted to struggle free of his demanding grip, but people were watching, aware and whispering, as she was led from the train and across the track to where a black and prancing horse was held by a man in a rather dishevelled uniform. For the briefest of moments she met his dark and sympathetic eyes, then the Don had lifted her into the saddle and with a supple bound had joined her and taken the reins. She at once felt his nearness, his muscular warmth, his infernal control over her and the stallion.

'We will see you later on, *amigo. Hasta la vista.*'

His friend the cavalry officer stood away from the horse and gave them a salute. '*Muy bien, hombre.* Good luck!'

They were off with a clatter of hooves, the breath catching in Romy's throat as a hard arm swept around her and held her firmly and inescapably.

CHAPTER FOUR

ROMY had heard of girls forcibly abducted while alone in foreign lands, but she had believed the tales far-fetched. She had never dreamed that such a thing could really happen, least of all to herself. Yet here she was on the saddle of a black horse, being carried across a country of rocks and shadows and savage sunlight, held within the circle of a man's unyielding arm.

She felt the trained muscles beneath his skin, and despite her fear of him she was impressed by his handling of the stallion, which was sleek and mettlesome. The wind across the *sabana* carried the tang of wild mountain plants, isolation, and mystery. The long vistas were broken suddenly by strange hills, clumps of cacti, and waving miles of esparto grass, which grew in places as high as the haunches of the stallion.

It seemed to Romy as if they were leaving civilisation behind and entering a region ruled over by the burning sun, the swooping golden condors, and the man who said she must pretend to be his chosen bride. All chance of escape had slipped away from her and her destination was firmly controlled by Don Delgado.

Her eyes smarted from the blaze of the sun and tears clung to her lashes as she followed the flight of a condor with outspread tawny wings.

'You had better tie my bandana over your head.' The Don spoke abruptly, breaking the silence between them. 'Take it from my neck.'

'I'm perfectly all right,' she assured him.

'Do as you are told, *niña*. Fair-skinned people feel the hot sun rather more than we swarthy Latins.'

'But you aren't ...' She broke off and twisted around in his arms so she could untie the bandana from around his neck. She had been about to say that he was golden-skinned, but in the nick of time she had bitten back the words. It would have been mortifying to reveal that she had noticed his attraction. He might well have laughed at her.

As she untied the scarf she saw the flare to his nostrils as he breathed the wild and spicy air, and she noticed how his eyes glinted as he surveyed the landscape. She wondered, just out of idle curiosity, if he had ever felt about a woman as he felt about the territory over which he had charge.

'Does that feel cooler?' he asked.

She adjusted the scarf over her hair and murmured her thanks.

'Say *gracias*,' he urged. 'I think you must learn to speak my tongue. *Gracias* is one of the loveliest words in Spanish.'

'I am grateful for the scarf, *señor*, but I am not Spanish, remember.'

'True, you are no demure dove despite the name of Romola.' As he spoke he deliberately tightened his arm so that she felt the iron muscles, the hint that she was at his mercy right now and had better do as she was told.

'This is all a bit melodramatic,' she said stiffly. 'Riding off with a girl as if this were the eighteenth century.'

'Have you not yet realised that in many ways Mexico is still a land of unchanged customs, whose people have their roots in a tempestuous past? Look around you at the strange rocks, at the cruel flower with its spikes. You love this land or you hate it, *niña*. There is no middle course.'

'May I ask, *señor*, if you call yourself a Mexican?'

'Not entirely. I was born in Spain where I grew up and was educated. My parents made a runaway marriage and they came to Mexico to live at the *hacienda* owned by the Avarados. The marriage was not a happy one and six months later my mother returned to Spain to the *estancia* of her father, where she gave birth to me. I grew up among matadors and bulls, for my grandfather bred fighting bulls for the arenas. I enjoyed going into the arena as a youth and I made quite a name for myself, but my mother saw the necessity for me to have a more lasting career and I trained for the diplomatic service. When my father died in an accident the *hacienda* was left to me and it was suggested that I become Consul of the region.'

He paused as if to let his words sink into her mind. 'I enjoy my work and my position here, Miss Ellyn, and I cannot jeopardise either for the sake of a foolish girl who took a journey alone and invited the devil's eye.'

'Your eye!' she retorted.

He laughed in that dangerously quiet way and she felt again the hardness of his encircling arm. It was as if the devil in him enjoyed inflicting this physical closeness which she disliked and shrank from.

'*Guapa*, you are going to be an amusing fiancée if not an affectionate one.'

'I hope you don't expect affection,' she said icily. 'I very much hope you don't expect me to parade false hugs and kisses in front of your family and friends ...' There she broke off as the horse shied in alarm from the great winged shadow that swooped suddenly above them, casting a feather that glinted like gold and then flying off with arrogant

55

grace. Romy was thrown back against the Don by the startled jerk of the horse and gripped bruisingly as he controlled the animal and urged him back into the rhythm of the ride.

When Romy recovered her breath and her ribs no longer ached, she asked if his mother lived with him at the *hacienda*. 'She is going to be surprised, *señor*, when you present an English girl as your fiancée.'

'Latin women, Miss Ellyn, are extremely tolerant when it comes to the peccadilloes of their offspring, that is if they are male.'

'You mean ... like everyone else she will assume that we spent last night as ... lovers?'

'You must be prepared for that. I am my father's son as well as hers and she will accept with gracious resignation that having committed Iberian rape I did at least bring the girl home as my bride-to-be.'

Romy turned her head slowly and looked into his eyes. They were wickedly amused, and she felt a swift inclination to slap his face. He had placed her in the most awful predicament of her life; she either submitted to his game of make-believe, or she became labelled as the girl he had seduced on a train. He wasn't even apologetic about all the trouble he had set in motion when he had walked into her compartment in his dark silk pyjamas.

She told herself furiously that his Iberian lordship needed a lesson, and he would learn from her that she was the one female who wasn't going to swoon at his feet.

Some time later they came in sight of the grazing grounds of the Valley of the Sun, an undulating *pampa* where the sleek cattle roamed and bent their heads to the rich grass. The Mexican horsemen who tended the cattle wore the *ruana*, a picturesque cloak that swept the sleek haunches of their mounts. They looked colourful and swaggering and they saluted the *dueno* as he rode past, and their sloping eyes dwelt with interest on the girl who rode on his saddlebow. It was a very Latin thing, a girl arriving like that with the Don. Some of them galloped closer, and as Romy sensed their curiosity she yielded ever so slightly to the man who had authority over them.

'Don't be afraid,' he mocked. 'They can see that you belong to me and are merely curious. The *vaqueros* prefer their own handsome girls with glowing copper skins.'

'Don't you prefer such girls?' Romy asked, with bravado.

'I am not a *vaquero*,' he crisped. 'Thank your stars I am not, because on that train last night I should have paid scant attention to your girlish pleas and made wild love to you. Do you imagine a *vaquero* would worry about slanderous remarks?'

'Hardly ... but if I had been alone with one of them last night I should not this morning be in the position of having to pretend that I want to marry you, a man I don't much like.'

'I hope you are not assuming that I like you?' He reined in the horse as he spoke and they were standing on the rim of the valley, so immense and wildly beautiful that Romy was lost for words. How lovely and limitless was the valley, and despite the doubts and fears which had brought her here, she would be able to explore it all on horseback. A tiny shiver of irrepressible delight ran through her.

'Are you so afraid now you are here?' asked the Don. 'I felt you shiver as if with apprehension.'

'It's the strangeness of everything.' She wouldn't admit how much she thrilled to the Valley of the Sun. She would be outwardly frozen, unstirred by the vista of coffee and cocoa bushes shaded by the immense leaves of banana trees. High above them stretched the great *sierras*, holding in their shadow the glitter of a lake.

'It is bridged.' He pointed with his riding whip. 'On the other side is the *hacienda*.'

'Your own moat and castle,' she murmured. 'Is there a tower awaiting your reluctant fiancée?'

'As a matter of fact there is.' He sounded amused. 'An *atalaya*, as we call it. A lookout across the lake and the land.'

'And what do you look for, *señor*?'

'In the old days it was bandits, but now they have gone rather out of fashion.'

'Have they really?' She spoke with a soft note of meaning in her voice.

He laughed with equal softness, and then he prodded the horse with a spur and they broke into a gallop that soon brought them in sight of the lake and the bridge that spanned it, stretching narrow and dangerous-looking across the wide expanse of sunlit water. Don Delgado set the horse at the bridge and when they were halfway across Romy saw how deep and current-licked was the lake. A person would have to know it well to swim in it or go boating on it.

She wondered if the Don often did so, when free of the duties that must take him all over the widely scattered villages and farms. It was his job, no doubt, to settle disputes among the Spaniards who had settled here; to see they were well rewarded for their labours, and to ensure that all went well with their families.

It had been ironical of fate to make her share a night with a man in a position of authority and power; someone who could not afford to become involved in a scandal.

Now they were across the lake whose shores were hung with wild flowers and mosses. Papaya trees curved on the shore and scented creepers sprawled in the tropical warmth. The silence was intense, without even the sound of a cicada. Only the hooves of the horse broke the silence as they cantered in through the entrance of the *hacienda*, which soared above them into a great arch, its pediment emblazoned with the family device ... an eagle with a dove-like bird in its talons!

'I take it you are unsurprised by the device?' The Don spoke as she stared at the pediment.

'I half expected something like it,' she replied.

'There is a legend in our family that an eagle

mated with a dove and a Spaniard was born.'

'Poor dove!' she found herself laughing. 'What a very formidable egg to hatch!'

'You must laugh more often ... green eyes were not made for tears.'

They cantered into the great stone patio, with walls as high and sun-gold as those of a pagan temple, weathered by wind and time, with palm trees and a turret rising above the patio, steps of twisted iron leading up to its parapet. It was like a minaret, with trailing plants down its walls and gnarled pomegranate trees clustered at its base.

Everything was so still, smouldering with the noon heat and the scents of aloes and coral-bush. Beyond the main patio were archways that mirrored fountains and flagstones, and the rambling walls of the *hacienda*, with red-tiled outbuildings clustered here and there. Then all was cloistered and cool as they came to the patio around which the family rooms were situated. Water tinkled in a fountain set with tiles blazing with colour, and upon slabs of cool stone were set great jars holding juniper and orange trees.

The place was Spanish poetry in stone. Romy imagined the scarlet swirl of a flamenco skirt against the old gold walls ... there was an undeniable magic to the Don's home which she could not deny to herself. Even a certain grace to the way they arrived, a man and a girl seated together upon a black horse.

He took his arms from around her and slid from

the saddle, and after hitching the reins to an iron ring in the wall he reached for her. As she was sitting sideways it was awkward for her to dismount and she was obliged to slide down into his extended arms. Her green eyes were blazing their resistance to him, and all through her slim body there ran the shock of physical contact with him. It was like an electrical charge, from which she still tingled after he released her. She knew from the sardonic smile on his lips that he had felt her antagonised reaction to him.

'I hope, Miss Ellyn, that my home at least will appeal to that cool artistic nature of yours. Do you think that it might?'

'It's a little too early to say. First impressions can be misleading, and you must make allowances for the fact that all this is very different from what I have always known.'

'I intend to make a few allowances,' he drawled. 'Your cheeks are flushed ... would you like to taste our water? It is piped from a mountain stream and very refreshing.'

'Yes, I am rather thirsty after that ride, and the sun seems to have grown hotter.'

'It's noon and the sun is high.' He approached the fountain of *azulejos*, on the rim of which rested a conch shell. He filled it from the fountain and brought it to her. 'Here you are, little *gato de monte*, slake your thirst and be welcome at the *hacienda*.'

She took the shell and drank the water, which

felt delicious as it cooled her lips and her throat. 'I ... I should like to know what you called me, *señor*.' She handed him the shell, which he immediately refilled and drank from. When he looked at her the lids of his eyes were half-lowered over his bronze eyes, and it was a curiously disturbing look.

'You are like the little mountain cat,' he said. 'On the defensive and quick to scratch. You make me wonder what you are like when you purr.'

'What nonsense!' She tossed her head. 'Are all Spanish people fond of talking in such exaggerated terms? Human beings don't purr.'

'On the contrary, *niña*.' He leaned against the colourful rim of the fountain, a striking and masterful figure in surroundings that suited him so well. 'There is a dash of the primitive in all human beings which our airs and graces and our clothes conceal.' His eyes flicked the leaf-green suit in which she looked so willowy. 'Our responses to each other have their roots in the law of the jungle, the sea, and the air. Perhaps in England you failed to realise this, but here in this remote valley you are bound to learn that I speak the truth.'

'Are you warning me about something?' She flicked the red scarf from her hair, which shone in the sun about her slender neck. 'Are you insinuating that I may expect primitive behaviour from you?'

He stirred, there against the fountain, and the spurs at the heels made a little chiming sound. Even his eyes held the full force of his Latin personality, the fire, the temper, and the glinting humour. He made no answer to her question, and his silence was far more disturbing than any words could have been.

'Y-your bandana.' She held it out, flaming silk to a bull. 'You must have patience with my fears, *señor*. It isn't every day that a girl is informed that she must masquerade as a stranger's bride-to-be.'

'Many Latin girls marry strangers,' he said, and as he took the scarf his fingers nipped hers, deliberately. 'But no doubt you have been reared to the romantic belief that love should come before the marriage.'

'I should imagine it helps, if two people love each other,' she said.

'Love? What a puny word it has become when people talk so lightly of loving a dress, a pet, or a picture. What has love to do with the battle of the senses that can rage between a man and a woman? "With love" is printed on a birthday card!'

'What a cynical viewpoint!' Romy backed away from him and didn't care if she annoyed him. 'Someone must have caused you to be disillusioned. Is that why you can regard me without any feeling?'

'I don't know, *niña*, that my feelings are unaffected when I look at you. Your colouring makes quite a contrast for a man who is accustomed to brunettes with dark eyes. Did the young man in the photograph never tell you that you have the hair and eyes of a small cat?'

'I don't like to be called a cat, thank you!'

'How do you think I feel about being referred to as a devil? Scratch a Spaniard, Miss Ellyn, and he will retaliate with a slap. He enjoys a fight, and regards a woman as an exciting opponent.'

'More exciting than a bull, *señor*?'

'Indubitably.'

'I suppose because a woman is more defenceless.' Suddenly as she looked at him Romy became aware of a feeling of curiosity; in the deep opening of his white shirt there gleamed a gold crucifix against the dark hairs of his chest. Had that strong body ever felt the cruel thrust of the bull's horn? Was that golden torso scarred in any way? Few *espadas* escaped without injury ... not that she cared if he had ever been hurt? It was just hard to imagine him at the mercy of anything ... except his over-riding pride.

'Yes, I have felt the *cornada*,' he drawled, reading her eyes. 'It was inflicted by a brave bull, I am glad to say, and you will be pleased to hear that it hurt like the fires of damnation.'

'I'm not so hard-hearted, *señor*! But on the other hand you must admit that it's a cruel sport.'

'It is a form of conquest, and to a woman all conquest is cruel. Even when a woman is to marry, she has this deep-rooted sense of being conquered, of having the sanctuary of herself invaded and mastered. All life, as I have so recently pointed out, is deeply primitive under the veils of perfume, polite talk, and civilised clothing. At the core of us we remain Adam and Eve.'

'And I suppose all this is the Garden of Eden?' Romy said pertly. 'I don't notice any apple trees, so I hope I'm safe from temptation?'

'Latin people believe that it was an orange which the woman offered to Adam, and if you consider it, *niña*, it would seem more than likely. Orange blossom is the traditional flower for a bride, and the fruit of the orange is much sweeter than that of the apple.'

'But you don't believe that love is sweet, *señor*.'

'Quite so.' His smile was slow and wicked. 'It is more like the *quemadero*, a flame which burns fiercely.'

'It sounds most uncomfortable, but then I have heard that Latins have a liking for martyrdom. English people prefer kindness and comfort, and as you have pointed out more than once I am very English, despite my name. Nonna, my grandmother, once said that my mother took the name from a novel.'

'Romola,' he murmured. 'You will have to grow accustomed to my using it, for I can hardly refer to my prospective bride as Miss Ellyn.'

'And just how long must we keep up the masquerade, Don Delgado?'

He stood there considering her question, beating time with his whip against the coloured tiles of the fountain. Romy felt that her heart beat in time to that whip, for what was a mere girl and her feelings to a man in whose blood ran the sacrificial paganism of the bullfight; who had faced the hoofs and horns of fighting bulls?

'Surely not longer than a week?' The words escaped from her in the tense silence he had created. 'I have to return to England, to my work and my studies. I can't stay here in Mexico indefinitely. I am not financially free to do so.'

'While you stay here at the *hacienda* you are not obliged to worry about money. Tell me, is your work in England so exciting; is your home life so congenial?'

'I like my work, and I live away from home in a bedsitter.'

'What on earth is a ... bedsitter?' He slowly raised an eyebrow. 'Is it possible that it is what it sounds like, a room in which you have a bed and a chair and a table?'

'There is no need to be so superior because you have an enormous house with countless rooms in it,' she said stiffly. 'You are fortunate, *señor*, but I am quite happy with my one room. I am happier there than ... anyway, it's my business. The arrangement we have come to does not include a résumé of all my past life and my expectations for the future.'

'Just tell me one thing, *niña*.' His whip hissed softly against the *azulejos*. 'Does your future include the young man who smiles in such a carefree way in the photograph you carry?'

Again she was tempted to tell a white lie, but honesty prevailed. 'That photograph was taken before he married my cousin, *señor*. He was a

66

friend, that's all.'

'Then there is little of real importance which calls you back to England.'

'There is my job!' She had to fight that helpless feeling of being at the mercy of this man's relentless logic; his determination to have his own way regardless of her desires. 'If I don't return to the museum when my vacation is up, then I shall lose it.'

'There are plenty of museums in Mexico,' he drawled, as if the matter of how long she stayed here was already settled in his mind. 'I have a certain influence and can always arrange for you to work among the relics of the past, if that is what you wish.'

'You always manage to sound so sarcastic about my wishes,' she stormed. 'Please remember, Don Delgado, that you are not my *real* fiancé and I don't have to take orders from you. I don't even have to go through with this crazy masquerade ...'

'Don't you?' A whisper of a whiplash was in his voice and he had moved away from the fountain before she realised and she winced as he caught her by the wrist. 'How do you imagine you will get away from the valley now you are here? Do you suppose anyone would invite my wrath and take you? Here at the Valle del Sol we are miles from what you probably think of as civilisation, and I am in complete authority. Do you really suppose I would introduce you as my fiancée only to have you walk out on me? Surely you know me a little better than that, even though our acquaintance is not yet of very long duration.'

'Yes, I know you!' She fought to twist her wrist free of his fingers and only succeeded in hurting herself, and this of course was fuel to her fury. 'Y-you are a tyrant and a bully. You are so used to bulls, that women are easy targets for your cruelty. I said before that I didn't like you ... now I begin to hate you!'

'Ah, now we really begin to know each other.' With an adroit movement he jerked her close to him and held her locked there, bodily, while his eyes looked down mockingly into hers. 'No man is sure he has made an impact upon a woman until she cries out that she hates him. You see, *chica*, to a Latin a woman's indifference is far more intolerable.'

'Y-you are intolerable!' She beat at his chest with her free hand and then stopped and blushed vividly as she felt his warm skin and the gold crucifix and the shock of touching him with her bare hand. 'I wish I had never come to Mexico ... since meeting you my holiday has gone all wrong.'

'Come, *señorita*,' his eyes held hers with wicked insistence, 'your holiday is not yet over and anything might happen in the future. You might even grow to like it here in the Valley of the Sun.'

CHAPTER FIVE

'DELGADO, *mio*!' The voice was deep and sweet, and Romy was released abruptly as the Don swung round and went striding across the patio to where a slender figure had appeared from the interior of the house.

'*Madre, qué gracia tiene!*' He embraced the woman and then kissed her on each cheek. There was love and delight upon the woman's face, and hands with flaming rings reached for his face, clasping his head, tears shining in her magnificent eyes. 'My son, how good to see you, and looking so fit. I have counted the hours, and when one of the Indians brought the news about the train I was worried. You were not hurt ... no, I can see you are fine. Delgado,' the dark eyes flashed in Romy's direction, 'I see you have brought a visitor. You must introduce me.'

Romy felt the beating of her heart as Don Delgado and his mother walked across the flagstones to where she stood near the fountain of *azulejos,* a slim and uncertain figure, about to be introduced as the bride-to-be of a man she hardly knew.

'*Madre,*' now he was standing tall and dark in front of Romy, 'I wish you to meet Romola Ellyn, whom I met in Mexico City and who has kindly consented to become my wife.' He reached for

Romy's hand and gripped it warningly. '*Amada*, I wish you to meet my beloved mother, the Doña Dolores.'

Romy had never been confronted by such a moment, when she must smile and force herself to look as if Don Delgado was the one and only man in the world. His mother obviously thought so, and she seemed such a charming woman that it would be a pity to disillusion her.

'I am so pleased to meet you,' Romy murmured, and with each nerve in her body she was aware of lean fingers holding captive her fingers, and of his mother's eyes searching her face in instant bewilderment.

'Did I hear you correctly, *hijo mio*?'

'Romola and I travelled together on the train, *madre*. She has agreed to become my wife.'

'You are pledged to each other?' Doña Dolores glanced sharply at her son. 'But what of Carmencita? She is here at the *hacienda* ... you knew from my letters that she would be here, and everyone thought ...'

'I cannot help what everyone thought.' His fingers tightened upon Romy's and she shot a look at him and saw how haughty he looked. 'I do my own choosing when it comes to a wife, and if you don't say something nice to Romola she will feel unwelcome and unhappy. She is English, *madre*, and extremely sensitive.'

'Of course you are welcome, my child.' Doña Dolores smiled with her lips, but her eyes revealed

70

how unwelcome was her son's engagement to a foreign girl. She must in her own youth have been a stunning Latin beauty; now in middle age she was rather like a severely beautiful nun, with a small exquisite rose hung on a chain around the neck of her grey silk dress. Her black hair streaked with silver was parted in the centre and looped into a heavy coil at the nape of her neck. Her rings intensified the beauty of her hands, and there was in her carriage, and the way she held her head, that same look of pride that her son possessed.

Yes, she had charm, but Romy could see that like Don Delgado she would be equally demanding. She had also his look of culture and aloofness, and Romy began to understand why he had been so insistent that there must be no scandal attached to his name.

'So, my son, you return from the Embassy the *amante* of a pretty English child. Forgive me if I seem rather overwhelmed. You gave nothing away, Gado, in your letters to me.'

'Our decision was a sudden one, *madre*. You might say that our feelings took possession of us and *presto*! we found ourselves engaged.'

Doña Dolores gazed intently at Romy. 'My dear, you still appear to be swept off your feet by this son of mine. You work at the Embassy, perhaps, and met him there?'

'No ... I was touring a-and we met in Mexico City during an earth tremor. Don Delgado swept me off beneath a doorway. I had never felt such a strange thing as a tremor before and I didn't know what to do.'

'So ... a *turista*. You like Mexico?'

'Yes, in a bewildered sort of way.'

'Just as you ... like my son, eh?' A smile came and went in the deepset eyes, reminiscent of the faint scorn with which Don Delgado had treated Romy's reaction to him. 'It must have been nerve-racking for you when the train almost crashed last night?'

'Don Delgado was with me ...' Romy broke off, furious with herself for blushing because the innocent truth had taken on such a guilty meaning, here in this country where a woman's honour was lost if a man was seen in her room at night.

Doña Dolores swept her eyes over her son's face. 'Then you plan to marry very soon, Gado? Here at the *hacienda* in the family chapel, perhaps?'

'We will think about it,' he replied, gripping Romy's hand as it gave a nervous jerk. 'And now, *madre*, I think Romola would like to have some refreshments while a room is prepared for her. Our luggage is at the train and I will arrange for someone to go and collect it.'

'*Lo que tu quieras*, Delgado.' For the span of a moment his mother looked as if she might weep or grow angry; she had obviously made hopeful plans with regard to his marriage, only to have an English girl introduced into her Latin household. With a restrained smile she asked Romy if she would like to enjoy her refreshments in the patio. The flash of

72

jewels on her hands was a subtle expression of her quiet anger as she indicated cane chairs and a table set beneath a pergola of wild golden cassia.

'It is cool there, *niña*. Perhaps you will take a seat while I tell Ana the cook to make a fresh jug of *sangria*.'

'Yes, take a seat.' The Don led Romy to one of the deep, fan-backed chairs, and it was a relief to relax into it. 'I will go with *madre*, if you will excuse me, and attempt to reconcile her to our engagement.'

'It would be better to tell her the truth,' Romy said hopefully.

He met her upraised eyes, mint-green in the shadow of the cassia, and wildly troubled. 'You are English and have not lived all your life with the many prejudices that embroider our Latin way of life. The Latin woman lives a secluded and rather guarded life, and it is important to her that her home and her children are never exposed to dishonour. This may sound outdated to you, Romola, but it remains a fact among my people. I cannot shrug off the implications attached to our night alone in the private compartment of a train. I must let it be seen that I wish to marry you.'

'Your mother doesn't wish it ... she made that very plain.'

'She was taken by surprise ...'

'Who is Carmencita?'

'Do you care who she is?' He quirked an eyebrow. 'Are you a little jealous as well as curious?'

'I'm far from jealous, *señor*! I just think it a shame that she and your mother must be made miserable because of our masquerade.'

'I have known Carmencita since she was a child. She is like a young niece of whom I am fond, and *madre* like all mothers would like her son to marry the angel who is known rather than the stranger who could be a Circe.'

'Do you think your mother takes me for a Circe, *señor*?'

'Very probably, as she refuses to take me for a devil.' He swung a branch of cassia against Romy's hair and studied the effect of the contrasting golds. 'Unlike yourself she is blinded by love.'

'Go away,' Romy said entreatingly. 'I have had enough of you and would like a little peace for a while. Go to your mother and assure her that I shall try not to be a bother.'

'*Niña*, she will expect to be bothered by the girl I am supposed to be infatuated with. She will be persuaded after last night that our marriage had better take place as soon as possible, so beware!'

'Y-you really have placed me in the most awkward situation.' Romy, driven by the impulse to express her fury with him, slapped the cassia spray out of his hand. 'And please don't flirt with me!'

'When I start to flirt with you, you will really know it.' A little flame burned in his eyes and menace purred in his voice. 'You had better beware of provoking a Spaniard, especially the one who in the eyes of everyone else is your beloved *amante*. It

74

would not surprise my mother or my staff if I were seen to chastise my tawny-haired, green-eyed *amiga*. With such attributes you cannot help but have a temper, eh?'

'I am sure you can be ruthless,' she retorted. 'The way you have dragged me here against my will is proof of that.'

'Come, *chica*,' he mocked, 'I didn't exactly drag you. I am sure you enjoyed certain moments of our ride as much as I did.'

'Such as?' She dared him with her green eyes to say she had enjoyed being held bruisingly close to him during that ride.

'Why, when we saw the golden condor,' he said mock-innocently. 'And when we arrived at the valley and you saw the lake for the first time. I heard you catch your breath, or perhaps I felt it. I sense that beauty appeals to you almost as much as it appeals to me ... can you deny this?'

She wanted furiously to deny the appeal of the *hacienda* situated as it was in a wild and wonderful valley, but his gaze was too penetrating, he read her eyes and saw that she was captivated by all this Spanish poetry in stone, tumbling flowers and sun-warmed tile. Her heart leapt and her pulses hummed just to look at the lion-gold beauty of the rambling house, whose walls had absorbed into their stonework the sunshine of centuries. Its ornate ironwork had surely come from the forges of old Castile many years ago, its Moorish-looking belfry held echoes of the desert blood that ran deep in the Avarados, and the shadows of window grilles and hanging lamps were as detailed as Spanish lace; strong as the ironwork were the rambling scarlet vines that burned against the golden stone. Each pendant leaf and weighted petal seemed to hide the heat-tranced cicadas and lizards, moving secretly with a flick of a tail or wing.

'To me this place has become the sweet breath of life.' The Don stood tall beside the chair in which Romy sat, a strong, vital figure in his riding clothes. 'It is built and cultivated as if it were a piece of Spain itself ... in the twilight when the chapel bells ring and the trumpet vines breathe out their scent in the dusk, it becomes Spain for me. I was born on Spanish soil, *señorita*, and my roots felt torn when I first came here. You will feel strange for a while, but in time ...'

'You speak as if I had come to stay, *señor*!'

'You think so?' The look he gave her was baffling, the lids of his eyes half lowered over the irises of bronze. Then he gave her that brief bow that reminded her of old court manners and the sweep of an invisible cloak. She watched him stride away, his dark head brushed by vines that trailed over one of the archways leading into the cool interior of the *hacienda*.

She sat very still until the fall of a petal upon her hand brought her out of her reverie. She knew now why his face had haunted her in Mexico City; even then she had had a premonition they would meet again, and from the moment she had seen him on the train, looking so much the haughty Señor d'España, she had known that Nonna's 'devil of a man' had crossed her path in no uncertain manner. As Romy put the fallen petal to her nose she had the feeling that Nonna would have regarded her dilemma with a great deal of wry interest.

Not even Nonna could have guessed that her legacy would lead Romy into the wilds of Mexico, into a masquerade she was committed to now she had met the Doña Dolores, who now approached her across the patio carrying a tray. She set it down on the cane table, and then sat down facing Romy. 'Have you ever tasted *sangria*?' she asked. 'Ours is made from a family recipe and is very refreshing.'

She poured it from the jug into long glasses and ice tinkled as cool against the glass as the words she addressed so politely to Romy. She uncovered a little dish of sweet cakes, and her eyes dwelt on the girl her son had brought home with him, taking in the red-gold hair that framed the green-eyed face with its blending of humour, compassion, and rebellion.

'You must forgive me, Señorita Ellyn, if I say that I think my son has been trapped by an unusual face. I don't want to play the embittered mother, but I always hoped that Delgado would marry a girl of his own people. A Latin girl born to understand a Latin man.'

'Are Latin men so different from other men?' Romy was trembling inwardly with nerves, but she forced herself to appear calm as she sipped her *sangria,* which tasted of wine and spices. She felt a rebellious stirring within her that the Don's mother should think an English girl unworthy of her precious son.

'They can be more demanding, more cruel and passionate than other men. They can also be most attentive and courteous, and you would not be the first young woman to fall a victim to the Avarados charm. No petticoat ever ruled one of them, though I understand that English young women like to please themselves.'

'I do please myself, *señora,* and I intend to carry on doing so.'

'Even when you become the wife of my son?'

'We are not yet ... married, *señora,* only engaged.'

'My child, you must know that you are already as good as married! Gado told me before I brought the *sangria* that you and he were together all last night, shut in your compartment which the engineers had to force open. He said the men saw you with him, and he is so well known, so respected, that he is under obligation to make you his wife.'

'I beg your pardon, Doña Dolores, but there is no obligation involved!'

'*Señorita,* my son must have told you that from the moment he called you his intended bride the people of this region would expect the marriage to take place. He not only governs here, but as a family we are traditionally proud.' Doña Dolores rose gracefully to her feet. 'I will not believe that you were not ambitious to marry a man who has every reason to believe that he will soon rise to the position of Ambassador. What girl could resist the title of Ambassador's lady?'

Colour flamed in Romy's cheeks. 'Whatever you believe, *señora*, I am quite innocent of enticing your son into my compartment. He entered by mistake ...'

'A very fortunate mistake for you, Señorita Ellyn. Please to finish your wine and cakes. I will send a maid to show you to your room.'

The *señora* walked away, leaving Romy almost on the edge of tears. So that was what everyone would think, that she had deliberately set out to entice the Don because he was a man with a spectacular future. It was unbearable ... despite its beauty this whole place had become unbearable and somehow or other she had to get away! She jumped to her feet and looked wildly for the way out of the maze of patios. She was too unhappy to think sensibly; she knew only a compulsion to escape from the *hacienda* before she saw Don Delgado again. Perhaps there was someone who would help her. She had money in her bag and could not believe that the men employed here were so afraid of the *dueno* that not one of them would take payment for helping her to get away. From what she had seen of the herders they hardly looked the nervous sort ... in fact they looked decidedly devil-may-care, and the Don had enjoyed telling her that if he had been one of them last night she would have been treated with scant respect.

This recollection brought her up short as she was running out of the *hacienda* under the great main archway. It was impossible! She couldn't bring herself to ask one of those *vaqueros* to take her to Xerica. She glanced around wildly and her heart leapt. A rather dusty station-wagon was standing in the shadow of the high wall, and as luck would have it she could drive; had been taught to do so because her aunt had liked to be driven to the shops and to her bridge parties.

Romy made a dart for the parked wagon and to her intense relief the key had been left in the ignition. She climbed in, started up the engine and swung out on to the sun-hot road. There might be a map she could study later on, but right now she was intent on putting as many miles as possible between herself and Don Delgado.

It would surely be more of a relief than a rebuff for him to find her gone. Neither of them had wanted this involvement and she was severing it in the neatest way possible, with no more pretence, no more unjust suspicion that she had behaved like a Jezebel. A flash of temper tightened her hands on the wheel and her speed increased, making a blur of the grassy *sabana* she and the Don had crossed on horseback.

'Hasta la vista,' she murmured, as the wagon sped over the bridge and the valley gradually receded behind her. It was beautiful, but not for her. It was a place she might have enjoyed, but not as the girl whom everyone thought of as the Don's bride of dishonour!

The petrol gauge dropped quite suddenly, in the middle of nowhere, and the wagon ran on for only a few more yards before grinding to a halt at a roadside whose desolation was almost complete. High above in the late afternoon sky circled a couple of big-winged birds, whose cries were curiously distinct in the silence.

Romy sat tiredly, with her hands still clasping the unresponsive wheel of the wagon. There had been no map in the dashboard and she had known for the past hour that she was lost, and with increasing dread she had watched the arrow of the petrol gauge and had tried to believe that before the tank dried up she would find herself on a main road with other traffic.

Her hopes were dashed. Twilight was falling, the warmth of the day was fading away, and she was stranded in the wilderness. It was no use telling herself that she should never have come to Mexico in the first place; that she would have been far wiser to have gone to Venice with a friend. No, she had desired to show Iris and Lance that she was heart-free and independent, and look where it had landed her! Far from civilisation, with nothing warm to drink and a gnawing place in her stomach, which had last seen food at daybreak.

Daybreak ... when the Don had insisted that she

go with him instead of staying with the other passengers.

Everything was his fault. He was the cause of all her woes. But for his overwhelming pride and ambition she would be warm and fed in a hotel at Xerica, not stranded like this. Romola Ellyn, English spinster of twenty, likely to be found one day a bundle of bones on a road leading to nowhere!

She fiddled with some knobs on the dashboard. Mexican music wafted from the radio, but now the engine was dead a chill was creeping into the wagon. Romy shivered and decided she had better take a look in the back to see if there was a rug. She climbed out on to the darkening road and stretched her limbs. The sky overhead was turning grape-blue in the afterglow of the sunset. Never before in her life had she felt so physically alone, and so in need of a hot cup of coffee. Bleakly she had to face the fact that it had been crazy of her to drive off in the wagon ... if she had kept her temper, and her head, she could have enlisted the help of Captain Javier when he arrived at the *hacienda*. He at least had looked sympathetic and friendly.

Romy sighed and told herself that regrets would not keep her warm through the coming night, and opening the rear door of the wagon she climbed in and looked for a rug. She looked in vain and finally sat there wrapped in her own arms, listening as something howled across the miles of cactus grass; watching through the window as the moon arose, full and tinted faintly blue. The moon tonight had every reason to look blue for her; it suited her mood, lost as she was, cold and hungry, and nervous of the surrounding countryside with its creatures that might come close to the wagon as the night drew on.

An hour later Romy was actively shivering and rubbing her feet and hands to keep a little warmth in them. Who could have believed that so dazzling a sun could leave the night so cold! She felt miserable enough for tears, and wondered in her misery what Don Delgado had said and done when he had found her gone. He had declared that morning that having named her his fiancée he would never allow her to walk out on him. Would he then come searching for her?

Tiredly she rested her head against the seat back and curled her legs beneath her. The night would pass more quickly if only she could sleep, and in the morning, in daylight, she would not be so afraid to cross those fields in search of a habitation. There must be people around somewhere, houses concealed by the undulations of the land. In her crazy haste to get away from the *hacienda* she had probably passed houses without noticing them.

She closed her eyes and tried not to feel the draughts that were stealing into the vehicle. She prayed for sleep, and it came at last in the form of broken dreams and a creeping numbness ... then in the very depth of night she seemed to dream of clattering hoofs, the chink of harness, and the rumble of voices speaking words she could not grasp. She seemed to feel arms around her, lifting her, and a cradling warmth into which she snuggled. Her pillow felt a little hard and she gave it a drowsy thump and settled her head more comfortbly. In the dream that didn't quite leave her a throaty growl of a laugh seemed to waft against her ear.

Moments of deep sleep can seem like hours, and Romy awoke abruptly from those moments to find that she was no longer in the chilly wagon, stalled by a roadside. She was in a fast-moving, comfortable car, wrapped in the heavenly softness of a vicuña rug, and held for double warmth in a pair of arms that were all too real, her head at rest against a muscular shoulder.

'Oh ...' She stared upwards and in the rays of the ceiling light she saw a set of features that might have been carved from fine teak, with shadows cast beneath the high cheekbones, eyes that brooded upon her face, a diabolical slant to the brows above them. 'You, *señor*!'

'Yes, *señorita*. Who else but I would bother to search for such a foolish runaway? My men, who searched with me, think me foolishly fond of you. Only you and I know the real truth of that, eh? We made a bargain and I will see that you keep to it; you will stay at the *hacienda* until I say you can go.'

'I ... I might have guessed that I couldn't get away from a ... a devil!' She might, in fact, have been grateful to him for finding her and making her feel warm and alive again, but he had to speak arrogantly; he had to let her know that only out of pride had he looked for her. 'What tale did you tell your *vaqueros*? That I went for a drive and mistook my way in a strange country?'

'I told them no such thing. They are of Spanish blood. They know that girls become frightened and behave irrationally on the threshold of marriage. They know you are English and not accustomed to having a master.'

'You will be lucky if you make me bow down to your every wish, El Señor!' She tried to look as scornful as her position in his arms would allow; she lay as tense and unyielding as a plaster figure. 'It wasn't fear of you that made me run away. It was being labelled a Jezebel by your mother ... she believes I chased you because I'd like to be an Ambassador's lady. The very thought of any such thing scares the breath out of me, and I am only too glad that our engagement is a charade and nothing more.'

'A charade, yet you ran away today.' His eyes held hers intently in the low, down-slanting light that reminded her of last night, those moments of panic on her bed, when if his face had come any closer to her, his lips might have touched hers and might not have withdrawn. It made her feel like fainting to even imagine those firm yet passionate lips taking and holding hers.

Suddenly, for all its smoothness, the sleek car was bouncing over the bridge that spanned the lake, and Romy felt the grip of the Don's arms like the grip of fatality.

'You will make me a promise,' he said, and there was a ring of steel in his voice; a glint of it in his eyes. 'You will not run away from me again ... this can be a dangerous country, and the next time you might fall into hands less patient than mine. Whether you know it or not, you are a most attractive young creature ... a wild young dove, whose purity I should not like to see tarnished. Do you understand me, *niña*?'

'Yes,' she spoke rather faintly, 'you are very explicit, *señor*.'

'Were you afraid, alone like that in the wagon, as if in the depths of nowhere?'

'It was the coldness I found most unbearable ... how can it be so warm by day and so cold by night?'

She shivered at the memory of those cold and lonely hours, just as the car swept beneath the great arch that bore the insignia of the eagle and the dove. In her tiredness Romy's thoughts were strange ... when he spoke of her purity did he mean to possess it himself? Doves were a pure white, yet they were also amorous birds ... did Don Delgado think of her like that, his arms around her as the driver halted the car in the courtyard of the *hacienda*, where lamps cast pools of light along the wide verandas?

Suddenly Romy could bear no more talk, and closing her eyes she pretended to be exhausted as the Don stepped from the car, then reached for her and carried her indoors. His booted feet rang on the tiled floor as he strode with her to a staircase. The stairs were not steep and soon he paused in front of a door ... Romy peered at him from beneath her lashes, the Spanish eagle bringing home the English dove and depositing her upon a great soft bed in a room redolent of sheets taken from lavender, beeswax polish, and the oil like incense burning in the lamps at each side of the bed.

Romy opened her eyes. 'Goodnight, *señor*. I shall be all right now.'

'Is there nothing you wish?' He spoke in a soft drawl, as if he read her thoughts in her great sleepy eyes.

'Only one thing,' she swallowed dryly. 'I'd love a pot of coffee, if it isn't too much trouble at this time of night?'

'You shall have it within ten minutes,' he promised. His smile was subtle as he regarded her, then with that brief bow that was both courteous and slightly mocking he withdrew from the bedroom and closed the door behind him. Romy slowly relaxed and watched a moth clinging with quivering wings to the bowl of the lamp at the left side of her enormous Spanish bed. The shadow of the moth was enlarged in its agony upon the smooth white walls of the room. It looked almost like a bird ... a dove, perhaps.

CHAPTER SIX

DESPITE her adventure Romy slept deeply and awoke to such a brilliant flood of sunshine that she knew the morning must be well advanced. She felt guilty, and then remembered that she was supposed to be the Don's fiancée and could be lazy if she wished.

She sat up in the vast bed that made her feel so small, and for the first time she took notice of her room. Yes, the walls were a sunlit white, with beams of a rich honey colour, and a crucifix of chased gold attached to the wall facing her bed. There were delightful things of beaten silver and mother-of-pearl on the wide dressing-table, and palatial cupboards for hoards of clothes! The floor was the same honey colour as the ceiling beams, scattered with creamy vicuña rugs. Red geraniums were banked in alcoves at either side of the wide, iron-grilled window.

Made vulnerable this morning by her recapture of the night before, Romy fingered the beautiful edging of lace on her sheets. By daylight she saw that gold-leaf glimmered in the deeply carved patterns of the woodwork of her bed. and the immense coverlet was of rich scarlet silk.

She didn't know whether to smile or to be awestruck. She, Romy Ellyn, always the outsider in her aunt's house, had slept in a gold and scarlet bed that might long ago have been slept in by a Spanish queen. She wouldn't doubt it. The very look of Don Delgado was an indication of how old and proud was this family whose roots were deep in Spanish soil and its history of past glory and conquest. It was no wonder he was masterful; a man whose pride could not bear the stigma of scandal; a man ambitious to be Ambassador.

Romy slipped out of bed and felt the silky tickle of the rugs as she went across to the window, that opened like doors on to a balcony that immediately put her in mind of a large birdcage. As she stepped into it she seemed to hang suspended above the patio below, and because this place seemed to have such an odd effect upon her imagination she felt again like a captive dove.

A reflective smile quivered on her lips, which curved into a startled oval as below her balcony there came a sudden clatter of hooves and the appearance of a horse and rider making for one of the stone archways.

Then as if he had senses always alert the rider glanced upwards and saw Romy before she could retreat into her room. The sunlit flash of his eyes caught and held hers, and the black sheen of his hair was like the sheen of the horse he sat upon. The white silk of his shirt threw into contrast the deep gold of his skin. He raised his whip and saluted her ... like some knight of old about to go jousting for his lady.

'Buenas tardes,' he called up to her, in his deep voice with its Latin intonations. 'I hope you slept well and did not dream that you were still lost in the wilds.'

'I had a good sleep, *señor*.' She was vividly conscious of being seen by him in her nightdress; it wasn't the first time he had seen her so lightly clad, but the garment was diaphanous and the sunlight was revealing. 'I ... I must get dressed ...'

'Of course you must.' His eyes were amused as they flashed over her. 'Let me say first that you look as if I had caged you ... don't, *niña*, make any more attempts to fly away. Remember what I said to you last night. The *sabana* is a wild place and some of my hawks have a liking for chicks who are so unfledged. Come down to breakfast when you are ready. I shall join you now I am back from my ride ... I have been looking at the bull calves.'

'Are you preparing them for the fighting ring?' She shuddered as she spoke, for his own strong torso beneath the white shirt bore the scars of his own fighting days. Her eyes flicked over the wide shoulders tapering to a supple waist and she felt a stab of emotion, almost as if it hurt her to think of that perfect male body tossed by a bull upon the hot, hoof-trampled sands of a noisy arena. How reckless of any man to dare to face such a duel ... but then she had heard that Spaniards were fond of a game of chance.

'My bulls are for breeding and for the market,' he called up to her. '*Señorita*, don't be too soft-hearted about life and its rather cruel ways. A grilled steak never hurt anyone, and I have watched football matches in which men have had legs broken from the kick of a so-called sporting opponent.'

And having had the last word he cantered off through the archway, and Romy knew without seeing it that a sardonic smile clung to his lips. She returned to her room and indignantly told herself that she was indeed a little fool to ever feel a moment of pity for such a high and mighty devil. She supposed that like most *espadas* there had been a flamenco dancer to stroke his cheek and flatter his nerve while he recovered from his wounds!

Romy explored her room and upon opening the door adjacent to it she found to her delight a bathroom tiled in black and white, with an enormous tub of luxury proportions, a shower enclosed in glass walls, great pink bath-towels, and flagons of tangy-smelling salts and talcum.

What girl could resist such a Bathsheba bathroom after years of sharing one with a cousin who never cleared up the water or the powder which she splashed over everything? Like a child with a new and shining toy Romy ran the taps and scattered a cloud of crystals into the steam, which immediately turned to a most enticing scent. She allowed her nightdress to fall around her ankles and stepped with delight into the deep tub. Rather shy in company, she often sang when alone, and the tiled resonance of the bathroom echoed to the warmth of her voice, most Celtic when she sang an old melody of Nonna's, just as her eyes were too green to be truly English.

Half an hour later she was clad in a lemon dress with a white collar that revealed the slim white line of her throat and the taut young bones of her shoulders. Her hair, still a little damp from her bath, she twirled into a Psyche knot and secured with a tortoiseshell comb which she had bought in Mexico City. Her eyes did not need the addition of makeup, and her skin had a pale honey glow. As she applied pale pink lipstick she wondered, not without a shrug, what the Don's views were on cosmetics. His mother was far too dignified and lovely to need them. Would he decide that his masquerading fiancée must discard the little paint that she wore upon her lips? Immediately in the mirror her green eyes held rebellion as she thought of his tendency to give her orders.

And now to breakfast.

She met in the hall downstairs the young maid who had brought coffee to her room last night and who had kindly helped her to bed after her ordeal. This morning, with only a few words of English, she semed to understand what Romy required and with a smile in her Latin eyes she led the English *novia* to where El Señor awaited her, in a small patio tucked away from the main bustle of the house.

He arose at her approach from a table set for two beneath a juniper tree, and he had changed his riding clothes for a suit of cool fawn with a thin chalk striping. It was tailored with the perfection he seemed to demand of all things, the shirt and tie beneath as crisp as his greeting.

'At last! Did you return to your bed for a nap?'

'No.' She gave him an indignant look. 'I took a bath and lost track of time.'

'Hoping I would have eaten and gone by now?'

'You shouldn't have waited for me. I'm sure you must be starving.'

'You should know by now, *niña*, that when I make a promise I keep it, I said I would eat with you ... do you object?'

'No ...'

'It will make things easier for you if you are seen to enjoy my company and I am seen to enjoy yours. Come,' a wicked glint came into his eyes, 'try and look a little more *enamorada*.'

'I feel sure, *señor*, that you have given everyone ample reason to believe that you enjoy my company ... after the other night!'

'The memory burns, eh?' He was laughing low in his throat as he drew out her chair. Romy slipped into it, feeling him close to her and avoiding his eyes and their mocking awareness of how she felt about him. 'Was the comfort of your Spanish bed better than a night spent uncomfortably in the back of a stranded car?'

'Of course,' she had to admit. 'Was your mother annoyed with me for causing you the trouble of a search?'

'As it happens I was a trifle annoyed with her.' He sat down facing Romy and his eyes missed not a detail of her appearance. They lingered on her hair, drawn back from the youthful hollows of cheekbone and temple. 'I have taken the liberty of ordering breakfast for you.'

'You seem to like taking liberties where I'm concerned, *señor*.'

'Men are notoriously bossy, as you know,' he drawled. 'Mmm, you are very slender, but I don't think you breakfast on a slice of toast and a cup of dark coffee. Am I correct?'

'I thought Spaniards took a frugal breakfast.'

'Many do, but I find that the air of the *sabana* gives me an appetite when I ride. After we have eaten we will go and select a horse for you. Please to give me your hands.'

'Why?' She looked as startled as if he had asked for her lips.

'Believe me, *niña*, I am not about to kiss them or to put rings upon them, not just at the moment. Come, your hands!'

She extended them reluctantly and felt the lean warmth of his fingers closing around them. 'Now you will grip my hands,' he ordered.

She did so, feeling the steely strength of his hands and the hard band of the ring he wore.

'Ah, *bueno*, I think you will manage Duquesa without too much trouble. She is, you know, the most beautiful mare this side of Mexico, bred in a direct line from the Arabian horses the Avarados first brought to the valley.'

'You are proud of everything you own, aren't you, Don Delgado? Are you not taking a chance in letting me ride one of your best horses? As I learn the terrain I might ride off ...'

'Into the arms of one of my *vaqueros*?' He looked amused, and yet there was a warning glint in his eyes, which turned at once to a suave politeness as a manservant carried a tray to the table and began to serve their meal. Romy watched wide-eyed the plates of delicious-looking sausages, kidneys, eggs, ham, and soufflé potatoes.

'I shall never manage all this,' she gasped.

Yet she managed quite well, and even ate the delicious slice of pumpkin which ended the meal. She sat back replete. 'I really was hungry!'

'You had little to eat all day yesterday,' he said, and he was lighting one of his thin cigars as he spoke, looking very much the dark-browed *grandee* who knew better than Romy what was good for her. He made her feel curiously like a child who had not been properly protected until his advent into her life. Fed, and sun-warm, her nostrils filled with the combined scents of the juniper tree and his masculine cigar, she was not unaware of a treacherous response to him. He was so diabolically attractive, as assured of a woman's needs as only a worldly man could be, and into the bargain he looked and acted as if like everything else at the *hacienda* she belonged to him. To a girl who had never really belonged to anyone it was an attitude which had a dangerous appeal.

She glanced away from him, disturbed with herself for liking even for a moment her rôle of *novia* to Don Delgado.

'What are you thinking?' he murmured.

'Why, don't you know, *señor*?' It was a daring thing to ask in the circumstances. 'I thought you could read my mind so easily.'

'No, only when you look at me, and right now you are studying every aspect of the patio except my part of it.' He puffed cigar smoke at a hovering bee. 'Do you find the patio to your liking?'

'It's very old-world and traditional, somehow lost in time.'

'Does it therefore not fit in with your modern ideas?'

'*Señor*, my ideas are not so outrageously modern as your tone of voice suggests. I admire old and lovely gardens, and houses steeped in history. I am not a superficial person, gliding from one thrill to another and quickly bored. Would I work in a museum if I were all that modern? You said yourself ...'

'Yes, I know what I said. It's just that as a Latin I don't like to see so young a woman travelling all alone. Is it true what you told me? There is no one, no relative, no lover, who cares what you do and where you go?'

'Not since my grandmother died. It was her legacy which enabled me to take this trip to Mexico. She left me a letter suggesting that I travel to a faraway place just once in my life.'

'And why Mexico?'

'I ... don't really know. It just seemed more

exotic than Europe.'

'It seemed to call to you, eh? Perhaps because your mother named you Romola, which has a Latin sound to it. So you were three years old when you lost your mother?'

'I ... lost both parents. They left me in the care of a baby-sitter while they went to dine at the home of my father's employer. It was foggy when they left, and on the way home a lorry ran into their car and they were both killed instantly.' She drew a sigh. 'Nonna always told me they loved each other very much, so in a way it was good for them that they should die together.'

'You are very romantic, *señorita*.'

'No,' she denied. 'I'm being realistic ... why should people in love be parted, with one left to grieve and to be lonely for years?'

'Have you ever been in love, Romola?'

'No ... yes, a little.'

'Calf love, of course,' he drawled, his gaze half-veiled by the lids of his eyes. 'With the young man in the snapshot. Well, it is good that you have got those slight pangs out of your system.'

'Why?' She looked at him because she had to. 'What business is it of yours, *señor*?'

'We are engaged ... betrothed, as my people call it.'

'We are pretending and you know it! There is nothing remotely romantic between us. I find you overbearing, and you find me foolish.'

'Don't get into a panic.' His eyes filled with those

97

wicked glints that made his bronze gaze seem alive with hidden fire. 'Like most men I have the desire to be loved ... why then should I desire you when you declare that you hate me? I should have to force you to accept my kisses, would I not?'

Her eyes found his lips before she could prevent them ... he had such masculine lips, the kind that would kiss without compromise, making a girl feel his passion to the marrow of her bones. He would be a masterful lover, demanding complete surrender from his partner. He would be passionate ... but would he be tender?

'I am reading your eyes,' he said wickedly.

Instantly she jumped to her feet and turned to caress a cat who drowsed on one of the low walls of ornamental rock. The Don was infuriating! With merciless charm he coaxed her into a mood of revelation, and then when she least expected it he mocked her youthful fear of him. He knew that a man like himself had never crossed her path before and he was enjoying the situation in his own sardonic way. Playing on her terror that he would make the demands of a real *amante*.

The cat arched its tortoiseshell back beneath her fingers and she heard it purring ... it was not unlike the sound that came into the Don's voice when he chose.

'Come, we will go to the stables and I will introduce you to Duquesa.' He took her by the wrist and for the sake of dignity, which he had ruffled enough, she walked with him through the maze of arches until they came in scent and sound of horses and a long line of stone-vaulted stalls. Dark-haired men and boys were at work among the stalls, polishing leather saddles and brasses, grooming the glossy-coated animals, and forking hay from a great stone loft.

Each man gave the *dueno* a respectful greeting, and in passing them Romy was far from unaware of the glances they gave her and each other. She caught their knowing smiles and wished the Don would release her wrist from his inescapable fingers. Last night she had obviously tried to run away from him, and this morning he was letting everyone see that she was firmly in his keeping again. A tingling pressure seemed to run from his fingers into her bones, and she was glad when they came to the stall marked Duquesa and he released her wrist. He glanced into the stall, and then turned sharply to one of the stable hands and spoke to him in rapid Spanish. Romy herself could see that the mare's stall was empty and she realised that the Don was demanding who had taken her out.

Then she heard the name Señorita Carmencita and a quick glance at the Don's face told her that he was deeply annoyed. He was about to say something more when a young woman in a riding-habit appeared in the stable yard, leading by the reins a superb, cream-coated horse who was limping badly.

Don Delgado's frown was like thunder as he strode towards the horse and caught at the reins. The girl, who wore an Andalusian type hat at a rakish angle, gave him a defiant look. Her eyes were carved at an attractive angle in her narrow, pretty, pale-golden face. 'It is only a sprain, Delgado. There was a rabbit hole and Duquesa cantered into it . . .' The girl's eyes flickered over Romy, and back again to the Don, who was smouldering with anger. She tilted her chin and the stiff-brimmed hat fell to the back of her neck, the strap stretched taut across her throat.

'*Dios mio*,' she forced a laugh, 'you look as if you might strike me! Have I done something so terrible?'

'You took out Duquesa when I had given explicit orders that I wished the mare left in her stall this morning. You told Carlos that I had changed my orders, and now you return with the mare in this condition. Explain yourself!'

'I wished to go riding and Duquesa is the prettiest horse in your stable.' The red lips pouted and appealed. 'I have a liking for her.'

'You have a liking for your own way,' the Don snapped, and it was then that Romy realised she could understand every word of the tirade and that Carmencita had spoken first in English as if to impress upon Romy that only a certain intimacy between herself and the Don could make him so angry. And the girl was alluring in her purple habit, with a froth of cream lace in the opening of the jacket, and tiny gold rings in the lobes of her ears. Her hair had a bluish sheen to it, and it was drawn back so tightly from her narrow, pointed face that it had the gleam of silk.

She and Romy were as unalike as two girls could be, and looking at her Romy could understand why Doña Dolores had desired her for a daughter-in-law. She was from the crown of her silky head to the heels of her high-arched feet as Latin and fiery as the Don himself.

With a Spanish imprecation he turned to the limping mare and took her foreleg gently into his hands. As he felt the tendons she nuzzled his shoulder with her honey-coloured nose, and he spoke to her in deep purring Spanish, a lovely creature he had obviously pampered and couldn't bear to see in pain.

'Return to the house, Carmencita, and be good enough to show the way to Romola. I shall stay to attend the mare.'

'You forgive me then, *amigo*?' The girl smiled audaciously.

'No,' he said shortly. 'You are a spoiled child and should have a sound spanking. Go with my *menina*, and please not to sprain her leg or I shall be furious with you.'

The girl looked consideringly at Romy, taking in her slender body and legs, and the style of her dress. 'I have been curious to meet *la Inglesa*, whom everyone is talking about. Come, I will show you the way and we will become acquainted.'

'In a moment.' Romy went up to Duquesa and fondled her bowed head; she was quivering slightly, a highly-strung creature who had been used by a rider in a bad temper, someone whose fond hopes had been dashed by the Don's meeting with an English girl. For a fleeting moment Romy met his upraised eyes and she was almost tempted to give him a smile of sympathy.

'Run along,' he said to her. 'Accidents will happen, as you and I discovered on a train journey.'

His words chilled her and she walked away from him with Carmencita, whose Latin audacity could not be dented quite so easily as Romy's sensitivity.

'You look quite upset,' said the girl. 'You British people are so silly about animals. It is a wonder that you can love a man who used to be a matador ... you are madly in love with him, of course. No woman can be near Delgado without wanting him for herself, and you have been very clever ... for someone who looks as if she has never been kissed.'

They reached the patio in which stood the fountain of *azulejos* and as they faced each other Romy wanted to tell the girl that she was welcome to the man who had disrupted her life and forced her to masquerade as his fiancée, but even as the words rushed to her lips she thought of the way his favourite horse had been mishandled. This Latin girl was not only spoiled, she was also inclined to be cruel, and Romy decided that she needed a lesson.

'Whatever you say makes little difference, *señorita*. I am the Don's *novia*.'

'Everyone knows how you came to be his *novia*.' Carmencita swung her riding-whip in a meaning way. 'But you are not yet his wife. Not a soul in the valley welcomes you as the future mistress of the *hacienda*. They scoff at the idea. To them you have no fire, no sign of passion, no streak of lightning. You are no woman for the *dueno!*'

'I was woman enough on the train.' The words left Romy's lips before she could stop them ... Carmencita stared at her, then with a sharp flick of her whip she flounced across the patio, where she paused in one of the carved archways and studied Romy. Suddenly her laughter pealed out, mockingly.

'Oil and water don't mix, *Inglesa*. Fire and ice are not happy together.'

She disappeared into the cool shadows of the house and Romy was alone but for the play of the fountain. She turned to gaze at the sunlit curves of water, and then she tautened as she heard the approach of masculine footsteps, firm and brisk on the tiles of the patio. They came closer and closer, and when they had almost reached her she swung round and found herself looking at the dashingly uniformed figure of Captain Javier.

'*Señorita*,' he smiled with his dark eyes, 'how nice that we meet aagin!'

'How very nice to see you, Captain.' She was delighted to see him, for at last there would be someone at the *hacienda* who would not treat her with hostility. She liked the reassurance of his uniform and had not forgotten how tousled and tired he had looked after a night of helping the train passengers who had been shocked and hurt. 'I hope you have come to stay for a while.'

'But of course.' He glanced around at the *hacienda* and there was a look of pleasure on his sunburned face. 'I have no real home except the officers' quarters at Fort Riera and it always make me happy to be a guest here. This time I am extra pleased because of the duty I shall perform.'

'And may I ask what it is, Captain?'

'Has Delgado not told you?' A smile flashed beneath his slim black moustache. 'I know, he is rather inclined to have his mind made up before consulting others, but that is his way and always has been. Like the tide to the beach he is not to be turned from his purpose.'

'Please,' she appealed, 'you have me in suspense. What duty has the Don devised for you, while you are on leave of all things!'

Luis Javier raised his eyebrows and laughed at her with a hint of indulgence. 'He has asked that I give to him his bride at the wedding between you. A duty I shall perform with some pleasure ... and some reluctance.'

'He ... has asked you to do so ... in actual words?' she gasped.

'Yes, he made his request when he borrowed my horse so he could bring you to his home. Are you not pleased? I assure you it will be an honour for me.'

Romy could only gaze at the Captain in speechless surprise. Don Delgado had no right to go this far, dragging his friend into the masquerade and pretending an actual wedding was planned. She was angry, yet at the same time she hesitated to blurt out the real truth to Luis Javier.

As much as she wanted to say it, something held her back from a revelation of the truth ... that in order to safeguard his diplomatic career Don Delgado had forced her to pose as his fiancée. That never ... never would she dream of marrying him.

CHAPTER SEVEN

No matter what the Don had intimated to his friend there could be no marriage without a willing bride, and soon Romy was able to laugh at the idea of the proud Don Delgado dragging a bride to the altar. In any case Doña Dolores was still very cool towards her and not so graciously ready to accept an English girl into her household as the Don had predicted. In her, as in her son, there ran a streak of iron obstinacy and though it made Romy's visit an awkward one, it also provided the loophole through which she could slip ... her English ways being so out of tune in such a Latin household.

There was one thing she could enjoy without reserve, the rambling, golden beauty of the *hacienda*, which in itself occupied acres of land on which stood the farms and stores and adobe houses of the many people who worked for the family. In every way possible it was run as if it stood upon Spanish soil. Its very odour seemed redolent of Spain, a blending of spices, coffee beans, and the carnations which stood in antique vases upon the carved sideboards and tables, whose sheen was like that of rich dark sherry which in the evenings picked up the glow of chandeliers.

Romy wished she were an artist so she could paint the *hacienda*, but she could sketch its patios, the flower-draped walls and lovely old fountains that splashed and gurgled. When she returned to England the sketches would provide a memorial of her strange visit ... she wished to make a sketch of the Don, but was too reluctant to ask him to sit for her. She tried sketching him from memory, but the subtle expressions of his face eluded her. No matter how she tried, she could not depict what lay behind his varying expressions; the essential man was too composite, too complex for her amateur talent. Yet still she tried to capture him, and one afternoon, when she thought everyone at siesta, he came silently behind her and discovered her at work upon his likeness.

'*Nos lametamos.*' He breathed the words as he leant over the back of the tiled bench upon which she sat absorbed. 'What a *mal hombre* I look! Is that how you see me, *mujer*?'

She turned a startled head and stared into his half-amused, half-searching eyes. 'Oh ... I didn't hear you, *señor*. I ... I'm trying my hand at some sketching, but I'm afraid my ambitions are greater than my expertise. Y-you have a difficult face ... oh, you know what I mean.'

'Do I?' He strolled around to the tree that shaded the bench and leaned against the many-branched trunk. It was a magnolia tree and it threw into relief his intense masculinity. He wore a shirt ruffled like a *gaucho*'s, and his trousers fitted his hips and his long legs like a dark skin. With his face partly shadowed by the tree, and clad as he was, he took on the look he must have had as a matador. Romy felt an ambitious aching to sketch him as he was, but with a slight smile she admitted defeat and closed her sketching book.

'You are too much an enigma,' she said. 'You would need to be painted by Velasquez.'

'You pay me a compliment, Romola. The first to pass your lips.'

'I merely state a fact. You are intensely Spanish, *señor*. Of a people who seem to remain as they must have been in the days of the Conquest and the golden galleons.'

'Proud, cruel, and intimidating, eh?'

'You said it, Don Delgado.' Her smile flickered to him and away, like a moth uncertain of where it should settle.

'How much do you know about the Spanish?' he asked curiously. 'Only that which you were taught in the schoolroom?'

'Only that, and the things I have seen for myself since coming to Mexico. When the Spaniards conquered this land they made it very much their own, didn't they? They imposed their beliefs and their religion upon the Indians. They strike me as a very imposing nation.'

He laughed deep in his throat. 'In other words we have the grand manner, eh? *Grandeza*. We like to rule and despise humility. But we are also able to bear great pain and sadness. Like everyone else we have our good side as well as our black. We are kind to young things.'

'But cruel towards animals ... oh, I know you are proud of your stable, *señor*, but you have fought bulls and killed them.'

'To fight a bull a man must be brave, or don't you agree?' He spoke half mockingly. 'That great angry creature can spit fire, believe me. His breath scorches the cape as he thunders by, and do remember that I was young at the time. Foolish just like yourself in entering an arena to face an opponent so much stronger and wilful.'

'You refer to you and me, of course, *señor*.'

He inclined his black head and his eyes slipped over her youthful figure in a white silk shirt and a scarlet skirt embroidered with yucca flowers. Her hair hung loose to her shoulders and she might have been a teenager ... but for the sudden flash of feminine fear in her eyes as he stirred like a panther in the sun and came to her with his graceful, silent strides, those of a man in the prime of his vigour and his awareness of the deep, almost primeval differences between a man and a woman.

In the moment when their eyes met, man and

woman aware, she saw in him not the *grandee* but the smouldering of this land, the free sky of the eagle, the *sabana* of the strong bulls and the wild winds.

'I want to show you my land from the top of the *atalaya*. You wish, of course, to come with me?'

'Have I a choice, *señor*?'

'You have, but it would be foolish to deny yourself such an experience for the sake of opposing me. I promise not to take advantage of our supposed relationship. Come,' his smile was not promising as he reached for her hand. 'It is such a clear day that we shall see for miles, as far as the blue peaks of the *sierras*.'

'I'll come, but you don't have to lead me there as though I'm a child.' She jumped to her feet and evaded the touch of his lean dark fingers, and as she walked with him towards the slender shape of the watchtower, flaring sculptured into the sky like a minaret, she felt the Don's sardonic side-glance.

The tower stood in its own tiled court, surrounded by palm trees and arcades that intensified its Moorish look. The cicadas shrilled softly in secret places, and at the corners of the patio wall were attached dwarf towers and stone lamps. There was a seductive air about the place, as if lovers might have trysted here when darkness fell; adding to Romy's apprehension in being alone with the master of it all.

Each time alone with him was strangely like the first time ... he was forever dangerous, subtle, unpredictable. They were close now to the fluted masonry of the tower and there beyond the meshed lace-iron door was a winding staircase, leading away up to the eagle's eye view from the rooftop.

'I shall go ahead of you,' said the Don, and there was a purring note in his voice which made her conscious at once of the brevity of her scarlet skirt and the slender bareness of her legs. Colour tingled in her cheeks as she climbed the stairs behind him, the sunlight striking hot through the arabesqued openings as they finally reached the balcony that overlooked the miles of *sabana* and the hot blue water of the lake.

Romy caught her breath as she stood beside the Don at the iron rail of the balcony and took in with wondering eyes the extent of his land and how tiny everything looked from this height. The white-walled villages in the valley looked like clusters of toy houses, the bull herds that sprawled beside the streams looked as tame as lazy dogs, while here and there the coloured cloak of a herdsman revealed him at rest beneath the shade of a tree.

The scene from this height was idyllic, and Romy had to admit that any man who ruled like a lord over all this would in the end develop a sense of power.

'Whenever I come up here,' he said, 'I feel a sense of peace, as if I had taken wing from my cares and responsibilities for a while. I fold my wings like an eagle and rest.' He smiled and rested his elbows on the parapet rail, and Romy's eyes were upon his profile as he scanned the valley in which grew the green acres of coffee and cocoa. Now while they were alone had come the moment when she must know why he had told Luis Javier that his duty would be to give away the bride ... she had no intention of being the Don's bride!

'*Señor* ...'

'Yes, *niña*? Is there something you would ask of me?' He spoke lazily, like a man who didn't wish to be bothered by serious matters just at present. 'Look at those peaks beyond that stab at the sky ... they are like the abode of the old gods ... ah, you should see them when it storms, when the thunder bounces from peak to peak, booming like anger in the throat of a god. The lightning slashes open the clouds, and the rain falls fast like the passionate tears of a goddess. At other times the peaks seem wrapped in a velvety stillness ... the love night of the gods.'

'I want to ask you something ...' She stood braced beside him, unnerved that he should be talking of love. 'Will you listen to me and give me a proper answer a-and not evade the issue?'

'*Niña*, I never talk of serious matters during siesta. It would be most unlike a Latin to do so. A Latin feels all things intensely and there must be a time and an hour when he can relax and not be bothered by argument or busines. Come, give me my hour of pretending that I have only the cares and concerns of a *vaquero* at rest in the shade with his *sombrero* at tilt over his eyes.'

'Would you really wish to be a *vaquero*?' She looked sceptical. 'You with your ambitions!'

'My ambitions, *señorita*?' He turned lazily to look at her. 'I have duties which I accept regardless of what I should really like. I envy the man who possesses but a horse and a saddle and the sun above his head. He is free; I am merely a master.'

'You love mastering people!' She gave a laugh. 'I can't imagine you riding the *pampa* at the tail of the bulls, or saluting another man as your *dueno*. You like giving orders too much.'

'I sound most charming,' he drawled. 'And only a short while ago you paid me a compliment and I thought you had become a little defrosted in our warm climate. I wonder what it would take to melt your English coolness? The treatment perhaps of a *vaquero*?'

'W-what do you mean?' Her impulse was to back away from him, but when she did so she found herself literally cornered in the iron hold of the balcony, which curved to the shape of the *atalaya*. With a step the Don had pursued her and she was trapped by his tall figure, and by the wicked glints in his eyes.

'Shall I tell you by what rule the *vaquero* lives? Fruit is sweet, but one must eat it or it perishes. Flowers are lovely, but they must be plucked or they wither on the stem. Well, *mujer*, what do you say to that?'

'Y-you don't leave me much to say.' Her eyes clung unwillingly to his smile that hinted at many things; the outline of his muscles showed under the thin silk shirt, and she knew him to be as intensely passionate and wilful as the men who rode for him. 'Except that you might want to seduce me because everyone thinks you have already done so. You like subtle games, and the one you are playing with me must be very amusing.'

'Amusing ... strangely pleasurable.' His fingers touched her hair. 'You flutter like a tawny moth on the edge of the flame ... you wonder what it would be like.'

'I do nothing of the kind ...'

'Ah, but you do, *chica*. Never were two people so opposite in temperament as you and I, and opposites attract like lightning to the lonely tree.'

'You seem to like making profound remarks, Don Delgado, but they are not always the absolute truth. You told Captain Javier that he was invited to our wedding—of all things—and now he believes that he is to give away the bride. There will be no wedding because you can't have one without a bride!'

'How very true.' The Don's look was mockery incarnate. 'But Luis, having no family of his own, holds ours in such high esteem that I could not let him think that I would compromise your honour and my own without redeeming it. I told him with a careless laugh that he could give away my bride when I married ... I named no names, *señorita*.'

'But all the same he believes I ... I am to be your bride!'

'We have a saying, Romola. "Don't run for cover before it rains." '

'Meaning I am getting into a panic?'

'Are you not? We have another, which tells a man not to look into the future but to enjoy tonight's moon, wine, and woman.'

'I am glad, *señor*, that the saying applies to the night-time.'

'It can just as well apply to the daytime. I am enjoying the sun, the view, and the girl who flatters me by being afraid of me.'

'I ... I'm not afraid of you!'

'Then your eyes are liars.'

'Th-they match the deceiving person you have turned me into!' Tears started to her green eyes and set them shimmering. Romy didn't enjoy deceiving his mother, whom she admired for her grace and beauty despite the coolness received in return. Romy, who could not recall her own mother, had always missed the special kind of love a mother gives and she had often witnessed the touch of a jewelled hand against the Don's lean cheek; the indulgent smile when Doña Dolores poured his wine or helped him off with his riding-boots. It was not easy for Romy to live a lie, yet because these people were Latin and aware of passion they would not believe the truth ... that Don Delgado had not made love to her during the night he had spent with her.

As he studied the tears in her eyes, his dark brows drove together in a frown. 'What are you asking with those tears, that I let you go? *Mi Dios*, a person would think that I mistreated you. Only today I was looking at papers and things in the family vault and I came upon something which might amuse you. I planned to give it to you this evening; a small token for being a good girl.'

'Don't speak to me as if I'm a child,' she stormed, brushing away angrily a tear that fell to her cheek. 'I don't need bribing ...'

'A bribe, you say!' In an instant his features had a look of menace, and pain shot through her bones as he gripped her by the shoulders and pulled her with sudden fierceness against him. His hand curved like a talon around the nape of her neck and her head was held immovably as he bent and took her lips and kissed them for a long time without any mercy or tenderness. His kiss was a total punishment, and yet even as he hurt her, Romy was aware of his arm like a shield between her vulnerable body and the iron of the balustrade. Even as her head spun she was conscious that he held her so she was moulded to his body rather than bruised against real iron.

'That time you drove me almost too far.' He muttered the words as he pulled his lips from hers and his gaze scorched the colour back into her cheeks. 'Now I have given you something to cry about.'

'Y-you have given yourself away as a brute!'

'Were you ever in any doubt of it?' He held her with cruel ease as she tried to wrench herself out of his arms. 'I really believe you would leap this balustrade to escape from me ... such a long and painful fall, *mujer*. Much harder to take than even my kisses.'

'It really gives you pleasure to play the devil with me, doesn't it?' Her eyes blazed into his, filled now with temper instead of tears. 'All your life you have had your own way and now you must have it with me, a-and I hate you for tricking me into coming up here. I hate your tower, your house, and everything about you!'

'To be sure,' he drawled. 'We have already covered that ground and the spikes of the cactus flower have already scratched me. You know, *mujer*, you really don't need jewels with eyes such as yours.'

'I can do without your flattery!'

'I only say what is true. Flattery has the ring of a false coin.'

'You have placed me in a false position, so your flattery ought to match it.'

'*Santina amada*, you really hate to be the fallen angel in the eyes of everyone. Well, there is a remedy, but I am sure you would sooner suffer...'

'Yes,' she broke in, 'I'll put up with anything sooner than marry a man I don't love, or ever could in a thousand years!'

'The point is taken, *chica*.'

He spoke soothingly, as if to a child, and this infuriated Romy. 'I hope it hurt you!'

'But how can a man of iron and ambition be hurt?' he queried, with a quirk to his eyebrows. 'Only those with feelings can have them wrung ...

116

do I seem broken-hearted?'

'You seem always a mocking devil where I am concerned.'

'And what would you like me to be ... attentive like Luis and stunned by your emerald eyes?'

'I ... I could hit you!' she gasped. 'You make me furious with your taunts, as if I am the one who compromised *you*. I shall be thankful when I can bow out of this farcical engagement and return to the cool sanity of England, where people don't cry "rape" just because a man is seen in his pyjamas with a girl.'

'How unexciting for the Englishwoman that equality with men has turned the bedroom into a public room.'

'It might be unexciting, *señor*, but you people are prudish about such things because you can't seem to trust your own passions.'

'I consider that I was very much in control of mine on the night in question.' He lounged back against the iron railings, scrolled to match the wall openings of the *atalaya*, and with lazy movements of his hands he took a thin cigar from his case and watched her above the flame as he lit it. His features looked even more chiselled as the smoke played over them. 'But only because you seemed young and frightened, not because I am a saint who finds green eyes unbeguiling. I begin to wonder if some of your insistent dislike of me is based on feminine disappointment that I didn't take advantage of your innocence. In fact you couldn't hate me more, could you?'

She just looked at him, racing around in her mind for words that might pierce the leathery gold of his skin. He gazed back at her, the lids of his eyes drawn down against the smoke of his cigar, taking in the youthful purity of her face, the delicate definition of the bones beneath her English skin, and the slightly rebellious look of the lips he had so recently kissed. 'Angel and tyrant, you and I,' he drawled. 'I could do no more than bring you here to the *hacienda*. It would, believe me, have got around that you were seen in my company in a locked bedroom. Even had I no reputation of my own to consider, you would have been pestered by men in Xerica. Mexicans live for *amor*, and you are pretty.'

'Lots of English girls look as I do,' she rejoined, resentful that his Spanish eyes could bring the colour to her cheeks. 'I'm not unusual.'

'Here in Mexico you are. You stand out like a tawny moth among tiger moths. Like a lily in a garden of poppies. If you don't know it, then you are younger than I believed and too modest to be let loose on the world. A cloister would be a better place for you than a train speeding through the Mexican desert.'

'I managed to avoid trouble until you walked into my life. When I first say you in Mexico City I hoped I'd never see you again.'

'Even your honesty is angelic.' He gave his deep purring laugh. 'I wonder why you were afraid to see me again? Did I make so deep an impression as we stood in a doorway and the earth threatened to open beneath our feet? If it had, *chica*, we should have been buried alive to remain immortally clasped in each other's arms. What an escape you had!'

'I agree.' She leaned her arms upon the balcony rail and gazed at the rolling freedom of the *sabana*, and she felt a smile pulling at her lips. If other people could hear them when they were alone like this there would be no question of scandal because who could believe they were ... lovers? Love was surely composed of sweet whispers and adoring kisses ... swift battles and breathless surrender.

'It all looks so peaceful,' she said, 'yet one senses a smouldering quality.'

'The climate of a country has much to do with the temperament of its people. Mexico is a hot country ... England is a cool one, eh?'

'My country has unexpected moods, *señor*. Sometimes we are lucky enough to have several weeks of blazing sunshine, but I prefer the autumn when the countryside is all shades of rusty red and sultry gold, and the sun seems to wear a smoky veil. Gorgeous, and all tangy with bonfires and fallen leaves. Secretive, rustling, with starlings strung out across the sky as the twilight begins to fall.'

'You speak with nostalgic affection, *señorita*.' His gaze was reflective as it dwelt on her face. 'We at last have something in common ... I often think of Spain and the south where I grew up. I remember the young bulls being driven across the plains and the drovers sculptured against the darkening sky. I remember the gypsy songs and the scent of bitter oranges. Can it be that distance makes the heart feel fonder, and scatters roses where nettles really grow?'

'You really would disappoint me if you weren't cynical, *señor*.' She flicked him a look as he lounged beside her, exhaling his cigar smoke in a manner too nonchalant to fool Romy. His stillness was too alert, like that of a swift and supple leopard. It might be the sunshine, or it might be anything that lurked behind his half-closed eyelids, and Romy was wary and trying not to show that she could still feel his hard kiss on her mouth ... a tormenting reminder that he could master her whenever he wished.

A wind stirred across the *sabana,* the first hint that the heat of the day was giving way to the coolness of the approaching sunset; it touched Romy's hair and the side of the neck, and reminded her of the long evening meals at the *hacienda*, when the various relations of the Don and his mother emerged from the suites tucked away all over the house, dressed in immaculate evening clothes, talking with animation, and kissing each other as if they had not met for days.

Romy had not known that such a feudal system still existed in the world, that a man of means should give home and board to the relations who wished to accept it. It amazed her, and amused her, and also made her own position in the household a pivot for speculation and rather embarrassing questions.

Tia Texeira had been quite scandalised to find that she had no box of silk and lace fripperies for her *luna de mielo*, and Romy had all but retorted that a honeymoon with Don Delgado was the last thing she looked forward to.

It caused her nerves to panic just to think of being a prisoner in those dark golden arms, and she was about to make an excuse to leave him when something cast a large shadow and there was a beating of wings directly above the balcony. The great bird hovered, then suddenly swooped as if to fly in over the rail ... as its talons gripped the rail the Don caught hold of Romy and dashed with her towards the stairs. He then snatched an iron lantern from the wall and heaved it at the eagle, which flew off with a cry, its wings spread wide against the deepening blue of the sky.

Romy stood breathless on the stairs, while Don Delgado remained at the rail and watched the eagle out of sight. Then he swung round and came striding to Romy. 'You have gone quite pale, *chica*.' He stood looking down at her. 'But I agree that eagles can be terrifying.'

'The talons, and the eyes ... so primitive.' Romy stared into the Don's eyes, then as if he might swoop upon her she turned and ran all the way down the winding stairs without pause, arriving out of breath in the patio where Doña Dolores was taking tea with two of the aunts.

'Romola, will you join us for *merienda*?' Rings glittered as a slender hand hovered above the teapot.

The request was polite and the thought of tea was inviting, but Romy wished only for the cool white walls of her room and its closed-in balcony.

'Thank you, *señora*, but not just now.' Romy's eyes shone green and delicately pointed against the pallor of her face, and she fled again as Don Delgado strolled into the patio. He would explain about the eagle and they would no doubt smile and shrug and say how timid she was to be the *novia* of a Spaniard.

She reached her room, across which the rays of the sunset were slanting, burning softly against the white walls and the golden crucifix. Romy sank across her bed and buried her face in the lace and scarlet cover. She was trembling from the reaction of the eagle ... and not a little from the Don himself.

Try as she might she couldn't forget the touch of his hands, the feel of his arms, and the fiery pressure of his lips. She was becoming frightened of what he wanted ... there seemed too much truth in the accusation she had flung at him, that he would not be satisfied until his seduction of her was a reality.

She must get away from him ... soon she must find some way to slip out of his reach ... at present he was playing with her, but there would come a day, an hour, when the mocking smile slipped out of his eyes, and his arms became her prison of warm, living gold.

Her heart thumped and a quiver ran all through her slender body. Never again would she venture into his ivory tower, where even in a *guaybera* and narrow slacks he had a look of lordly assumption over her person. Even with her eyes tightly closed she could still picture his face, which had the strength of sculptured gold, with long brows which seemed to tally with the strong line of his nose. His lean jaw was implacable ... it was his mouth that gave him away as a passionate man.

His mouth which had taken hers almost with ravishment.

CHAPTER EIGHT

THE wind had risen all of a sudden and by the time Romy was dressed for dinner it was rasping across the golden miles of *sabana*, and beating against the stone walls of the *hacienda*. She had already experienced an earth tremor in Mexico, and tonight a whirling wind had arrived, so that maids had spent the past hour running from room to room fastening shutters and throwing sheets over the furniture.

As Romy coloured her lips she felt the dust with the tip of her tongue and grimaced at her reflection in the mirror, which was lamplit owing to the switched off electrical supply. Wires and poles could be torn down and the roofs of the barns were thickly thatched and a fire could cause damage and death to the livestock. The Don had given his orders ... lamplight for the bedrooms, candlelight for the dining table!

Romy looked herself over in the mirror ... Spanish people were so meticulous about their own appearance, and she honestly believed they would sooner go hungry than not have a smart suit or dress to wear, and a good piece of jewellery, whether it be a diamond brooch in a *mantilla* or gems at the cuffs of a speckless white shirt.

Romy wore this evening a limpid green dress with an oval neckline, and she wore also several dabs of her precious *Blue Grass* perfume. Her satin high-heeled shoes were the same colour as her dress and she felt rather chic, and looked coolly English with her tawny hair clipped into soft swirls at either side of her jawline. Across the lids of her eyes she had applied a slight hazing of silvery green. It wasn't that she was trying to look glamorous; she needed to appear in cool control of herself, in contrast to the confused young creature who had fled from Don Delgado that afternoon.

As she turned from the mirror she met the wrinkle-faced gaze of a lizard which uttered a small strange cry from its perch on top of the wardrobe. Tonight many tiny animals would take refuge from the wind inside the strong walls of the *hacienda*, and as Romy listened to the wind she couldn't help but feel a sense of security herself, enclosed within the walls which had withstood the variations in the Mexican weather for several centuries.

There was even a romantic isolation to the place ... like a castle of olden days it held all the members of a single family, and all the retainers of that family. They were shielded by its great roof and watched over with authority by the Don ... she alone held an equivocal position in his house.

But Romy didn't want to think about that and she tried to stem her thoughts by crumbling a biscuit for the lizard and lingering in her room until she heard voices passing in the corridor. Now she could go down and not be caught alone by the Don. He was always first in the *cuarto de estar* to greet everyone, and tonight Romy wanted not a moment alone with him.

As luck would have it she met Luis Javier and they made their way downstairs together. 'Is this wind likely to get worse, Captain?' she asked. 'I'm thinking of the coffee and cocoa bushes and the damage likely to be done.'

'The plantation is shielded by the valley walls, and these winds sometimes sound more furious than they are.' He shot her a smile. 'Anyway, it feels good to be here at the *hacienda* and not out riding in it. The company is fine and we shall eat an excellent dinner and drink the best of wines. What more could we ask?'

'You make it sound like a party.' And she was

laughing as they entered the *cuarto de estar*, to become immediately the focus of the Don's eyes. He stood a head taller than the other men present in the room, clad in a dark suit tailored to fit him like a glove. Above his head, shining against panelling like old silk was a gem-encrusted Aztec mask, and Romy chose to look into the eyes of the mask rather than into the eyes which swept from her hair to the tips of her satin shoes.

Everyone had been talking excitedly, with that hint of emotion which is aroused when danger lurks in the night. There were flowers everywhere, and lamps that flickered whenever the wind shook the shutters. Eyes held a glimmering brightness and lace fans moved restlessly ... everyone was enjoying the danger, and yet there was also fear in the air. Tonight the women's dresses were gayer, and Carmencita looked almost like a lovely Indian girl in her frilled blouse and flounced skirt of flamingo pink. Her hair shone like watered silk and was arranged into intricate loops and twirls and plaitings, so that her slender neck seemed as if it might snap under the shining weight. Her long lashes curled away from her almond eyes as she stared at Romy. In the lobes of her ears hung gleaming gold earrings.

Romy caught the message that flashed in the Latin eyes. She, Carmencita Revelde, was made for a man such as the Don, and she would do anything to take him away from an English girl who seemed always distant with him.

'How charming you look, Carmencita.' Romy meant every word, but the Latin girl refused to return her smile. Her dark eyes smouldered with resentment as they took in the tawny fairness and green-clad slimness of the girl who had come as a stranger to be the *dueno*'s bride.

'*Silencio, por favor!*' The Don was holding up his hand, and at once the chatter died away. 'I have something to give to my *novia* which I have only just found in the family vaults. I wished to make the presentation in private, but I have been so busy all the evening that the moment slipped by. Romola, will you come to me?'

Romy's cheeks burned as all eyes turned to look at her. She couldn't move and was ready to hate him for paying her such deliberate attention in front of his family. Of all the eyes upon her, it seemed that his mother's were the most intent. She knew, as Romy knew, that he was fastening more tightly about her the arms that didn't really love her. Never before in his life had any female opposed him as she did, and he was subtle as an inquisitor in his punishment.

'The Doña Romola appears to be reluctant.' Carmencita gave a taunting laugh, and the golden hoops swung against the creamy-gold of her bare neck. She would have leapt to claim whatever he had to offer, and Romy wanted to cry out that she was welcome to his gifts.

All at once he moved and strode gracefully towards Romy. He wore his most charming smile, but deep in his eyes there glittered that look of a leopard about to leap upon its prey. Romy's eyes implored him not to come any closer, but already he was towering above her, his chin jutting firm and hard above her head. 'Please to give me your hand, *amiga*. Come, don't hide it behind you as if I mean to bite you.'

She longed to defy him, yet she yielded to him because all the family watched and it would have been humiliating to be forced by him to surrender her hand. He took her wrist in his supple fingers and she felt their pressure against her racing pulse. His eyes flicked her face. 'So nervous of me?' he murmured, for her ears alone. The look she gave him was defiant as he locked about her wrist a bracelet of gems almost the same shade of green as her eyes. Her heart missed a beat ... Spaniards did not give rings, they gave a betrothal bracelet, and Romy could tell from the gasp that ran from person to person that she had guessed what he was doing.

'And now the necklace,' he said, and she knew it would be no use to protest ... it would be like begging mercy of the wind storm that raged around the *hacienda*. 'I shall not disturb your hair too much, *niña*.' His hand swept aside her tawny hair and she was helpless to defend herself against his intention. A necklace to match the green gems was clasped about her throat, sending out glimmering sparks that shocked her as much as the brush of his fingers against her skin. She had thought he was giving her beryls, but when she looked into his half-mocking eyes she knew differently.

'My child,' Doña Dolores came gracefully across the room, surely acting out the pleasure she didn't really feel as she took Romy's face between her ringed hands and kissed her on both cheeks. 'The family emeralds become you! You have eyes that almost match their colour and their lustre. Are you pleased with them?'

Romy gave the bracelet a glance of panic, and yielded to a smile which ached on her mouth. 'It's kind of Don Delgado to let me wear such valuable jewels ...'

'They will be yours when you marry Delgado, but it is nice during the *noviazgo* for some of the jewels of the family to be displayed by the *novia*, and I am pleased that you are *guapa* for my son ... how do you say? ... good-looking, with your fair skin and shining hair.'

Romy's fair skin took a blush very easily and though she knew that Doña Dolores was being gracious because all the family watched this ritual, it was nonetheless welcome. This was a family of strong, proud, explosive passions, and it was for their benefit that the Don presented the jewels. He meant to play his part of *novio* to the very hilt, and Romy was too sensitive, too reserved, to make a fuss in front of a roomful of relatives. For the sake of his mother's pride in him she had to tolerate his air of proprietorship.

He pinched her earlobe and shot a quizzical

smile at the assembled company. 'This time I take more than the ear,' he quipped.

'And she is prettier than any young bull, *amigo*,' laughed one of the uncles. 'He was an artist with the cape, Romola, this man that you will marry. He teased the bulls to within a fraction of his torso and everybody held their breath ... Delgado, will you ever fight in the arena again?'

'No, *tio*, that kind of fighting is over now.' The Don's eyes flicked the face of his supposed fiancée. 'I enter now for a different kind of *corrida*.'

The men laughed, while the ladies smiled behind their fans.

'A moment of truth even more exciting, eh?'

'Exactly so,' drawled the Don. 'And now I think we will go in to dine before the *gazpacho* becomes warm.'

The *gazpacho* was a delicious cold soup, creamy and tangy, and served with little dishes of savoury ham, juicy olives, and sliced tomato. Everybody ate with gaiety and hunger, while the wind outside seemed with fury to hurl itself at the shuttered entrances, shaking them and whining at the keyholes, and making dance the candle flames in the candelabra of silver scrolled with Inca patterns. The interior walls of the dining *sala* were covered with a rich velvet of a startling and lovely design ... eagles and foliage and exotic fruits.

The room made a perfect setting for vivid Latin faces, high fluted combs holding the perfumed hair of the ladies, and the gleam of dark, proud, yet humorous eyes.

The Don sat at one side of the great carved table, while his mother the *madrina* faced him. The conversation was vivacious, in a mixture of Spanish and English, and each time the Don spoke in his deep voice, both musical and merciless, Romy had to admit that he dominated the company. Mysterious and ineffable was the spell he could weave, intensified by the candlelight as it stroked the proud, high bones of his face.

'We are all safely gathered in the *alcazar* of our Don.' Tio Isidro raised his wine glass to his nephew. '*Salud.*'

Covers were lifted from enormous dishes and out wafted spicy odours. Roast pork crackled as it was carved, baked onions stuffed with meat and rice were served, along with sweet potatoes and plump green beans. Everything came from the estate and every dish was cooked with the perfection demanded by the Don.

Tonight his range of nieces and nephews (he was by courtesy their *tio*) sat with their parents at the table and listened wide-eyed to the conversation. Romy had to smile a little. How feudal in some ways were these people, yet how worldly in others. No subject, however intimate, was kept out of earshot of these children, while the Don seemed to enjoy tossing them fondants, not to mention fond remarks.

He was the *dueno*, and Romy was very sure that he revelled in his status. Suddenly a silver-wrapped sweet landed in her lap, and when she looked at him he quirked an eyebrow.

'What are you thinking, Romola? That we are of the Middle Ages? That unlike more sophisticated nations we cling to family traditions and like to eat and talk and laugh together all under one roof?'

'I . . . I rather like it.' She was too honest to deny the appeal of this large, vital, good-looking clan of Spaniards, and after two glasses of the rather potent Spanish wine she might even have said that it was enormously generous of Don Delgado to give so many relatives such a good home. Even if it made him feel the grand gentleman, it was still undeniably good of him.

'Yes, Tia Felicitas,' he bent his ear to one of the more elderly aunts, who wore a silken shawl with long fringes, 'my English *novia* is in sympathy with our tradition of closeness within the family circle. She has no such family herself and has been rather alone.'

'Then, Delgado, it is good that you make her a member of ours.' Tia Felicitas gave Romy a considering look. 'We are proverbially proud, child. Our traditions survive because we honour the family and have men such as Delgado to protect us when we grow old, or find ourselves homeless. It is part of our Moorish heritage.'

Tio Isidro heard this remark and joined in. 'They gave us the bullfight, *niña*, and also the instinct to keep our women in secluded fountain courts. They gave us our music, our fear of hell and our hope for paradise.'

'You speak like a poet, *señor*.'

'A Spaniard is always a poet by candlelight ... it brings out the lover and the mystic in him.'

She smiled into the dark and twinkling eyes and thought that Tio Isidro had quite a dash of the romantic Arab in him. She ate the candied green-gage which the Don had tossed her, and dared not look at him for confirmation of his uncle's remark. Let him play the lover and mystic in the direction of Carmencita, who was looking at him as if he were the only man in the room.

Romy turned to Luis Javier and asked him if there was any chance of going boating on the lake when the weather settled down again. 'I've seen the Indians fishing in the deep parts and I'd love to sail across to that small island ... the one with the sacrificial stone.'

'It is always deserted, Romola. The Indians won't go near it.'

'Will you, Luis?' Her green eyes glowed in her slender face. 'I'd very much like you to take me there.'

'Why?' He leant a little towards her and his eyes were serious. 'Do you think it would make Delgado angry with you, to be alone with me? Do you look for an excuse not to marry him?'

'Yes ... he begins to frighten me ... as if he really means ...' She bit her lip and fingered the bracelet on her wrist, shafting its green fire into her frightened heart. 'His code of honour means more than anything to him, and you must have guessed that nothing happened between us that night on the train.'

'I did guess,' said Luis in a voice as confidential as hers.

'But he insisted on bringing me here, and now he decks me out in part of the family heirlooms ... where will it all end? How will I get away, Luis, if I become too involved with this patriarchal family? A point of honour brought me here, so why can't another help me to get away? I know you are the Don's best friend ... I'm sure you wouldn't want to see him tied by Spanish law to a woman he doesn't really love ...'

Luis played with the stem of his wine glass, and a glance at his serious, duty-marked face kindled a spark of hope in Romy's breast. He was the only person here who could help to snatch her like a brand from the burning. He valued the Don as a friend, but he knew how proud he was. Romy was certain she would be sacrificed to that pride unless someone helped her, and she implored Luis Javier with her large green eyes to be that person.

'Take me to the island, Luis. Let everyone think that I ... like you better than the Don.'

'It might blemish the friendship he has for me.'

'I'm sure that it won't! It isn't as if the Don cares for me. He's playing a game of make-believe, and something must be done before we are both trapped into a marriage that would be a disaster. You know how things can get out of hand. How one wrong step can lead to another, until there is no turning back. Help me not to let that happen. I ... I know I'm asking a lot of you, but there is no one else I can ask. If I rode away he would follow me, and I don't know the country well enough to evade him. The best way is for me to hurt that darned pride of his, or to appear as if I do, then he'll let me go ... the English Miss who couldn't resist flirting with his friend.' She broke into a smile. 'There is a belief, Luis, that English girls are unable to resist a man in a uniform.'

'I think, *señorita*,' Luis raised his wine glass to her, 'that you are the sort of girl who would love a man for reasons of the heart rather than the eye.'

'You are kind to say so, Captain.'

'And you really wish me to take you to this pagan little island ... to make it appear that you like to be alone with me?'

'I like your company, Luis. There would be no real deception involved.'

'Only a blow to Delgado's pride, eh?'

'Exactly. How could such a man, who might possibly become Spanish Ambassador, take for a wife a girl of untrustworthy instincts?'

Luis looked gravely at her. 'I have a great regard for Delgado ... are you certain he is not fond of you?'

'Absolutely. He plays with me ... as you see him now playing with Loreta.'

Luis followed her glance across the table, to where the Don held the youngest member of the family in the crook of his arm while he fed her with cream cake. Her glossy hair shone against the sombre darkness of his sleeve, and Romy steeled herself against the appeal of the scene. He was a Spaniard, so he was fond of children ... he would want them when he married, but they mustn't be the offspring of a marriage resulting from a false step taken into her compartment on a night reserved by the fates for a fall of rock on the railway lines. Like the wheels of that train she and this man were heading for trouble ... unless a diversion of some sort was created.

When dinner came to an end the adults returned to the *cuarto de estar* for coffee, while the children were taken to bed by their nursemaids. First of all they had kissed everyone, including Romy, and feeling more shaken than ever she took a chair on the fringe of the family circle and tried to look as distant as possible. She wasn't one of them, and they mustn't behave as if she were, with those knowing glances at the emeralds around her neck and her wrist. She wished the evening would end so she could remove them ... she wished she had the courage to walk out of the room right now, but the Don would only come after her; she saw it in his eyes as they settled on her, there in the shadowy part of the lamplit room.

Was he remembering their hour alone on the roof of the *atalaya*, as she was? Though he looked the well-groomed *hidalgo* tonight, she kept seeing him as he had looked in his *guayabera*, whose chamois colour had been darker than his skin. When he made charming remarks to this aunt or that one, Romy was feeling again the primitive anger of those same lips on hers, kissing her as if to punish her for ever coming to Mexico.

'That wind is really too persistent,' said Doña Dolores. 'I hear a loose shutter banging somewhere and I must go and see to it. Delgado, perhaps some music to drown the wind?'

'Of course, *madre*, but first some *queimada* to help us forget that the wind attacks the *hacienda* with the fury of a locked-out soul. Tio Isidro, you will assist me with this cure for the blues?'

'Only too willingly. We need *coñac*, a lemon squeezed in the fist, brown sugar, and a bronze bowl.'

When the *queimada* was prepared a flame was applied to it, leaping azure to add a glint of devilry to the Don's eyes as he carried round the tray of glasses.

At last he paused in front of Romy. 'You look rather blue tonight, *niña*, despite the emeralds. Try some of this and try to relax ... you are as tense as you were the first time we met.'

'And with good reason,' she rejoined, hating the tremor in her fingers as they clasped the brandy glass. 'I don't want your jewels ... if it was your intention to make me feel a thorough cheat, then you have succeeded.'

'A cheat, *niña*?'

'Yes ... a miserable phoney.' Her eyes met his with rebellion in them, and a hint of pleading. 'Y-you aren't playing a fair game, *señor*. Gems of betrothal were not in our bargain.'

'Most women love jewels, especially when they match the eyes of the wearer. You should take a look at yourself. You hardly look a girl who plans to spend her life in a museum.'

'You won't alter my plans, Don Delgado.' The tremor had reached her voice. 'I ... I know that you are doing all this as a sort of punishment ... paying me back for travelling on my own and landing you in a spot. I won't apologise for something I couldn't help ...'

'Hush, *niña*. The family will think we are quarrelling.'

'I absolutely hate you!' Her eyes duelled with his. 'I warn you ...'

'I shouldn't if I were you, *niña*.' The lids of his eyes held a menacing weight to them, and then he walked away from her, with an arrogance she swore to shake to its foundations. How dared he assume rights over her that were only permissible within the bonds of a declared love and a mutual desire for union!

Romy gasped as the strong brandy raced down her throat and spread its fire through her veins. She jumped to her feet and would have run from the room, but suddenly Luis was by her side and he was gripping her hand. 'No,' he said, 'this is not the moment to run away. Look, two of the boys are going to play the guitar ... ah, and we are to have some dancing!'

A combination of nerves and brandy made Romy's legs feel weak; she wanted to lean against Luis as Carmencita ran to the centre of the room, holding her flounced skirt in her hands and revealing the scarlet heels of her shoes.

Flamenco, exciting and sensuous as only a Latin girl could dance it, her dark eyes flashing signals at Don Delgado and seeing no one else in the room ... she might have forgotten Romy until with a sudden pounce she grabbed her arm and forced her away from Luis. She dragged her to the centre of the room. 'Dance as I dance, English girl! Come, show us if you have spirit and fire!'

'Let me go!' Romy fought with the girl, and abruptly hands were beneath her armpits and she was being lifted like a doll. There was laughter. The relatives thought it just a game, but for Romy it was humiliation as the Don carried her from the room as if he could no longer wait to be alone with her. He was laughing as the music followed them, then they were alone as abruptly as they had been the focus of all eyes. A door closed with a thud and shut them together in his sanctum, a place of rich dark walls, Goyas in carved frames, and the decorative killing swords and golden capes of his *espada* days.

When he had first taken hold of her she had been too stunned to put up a fight, but now she began to do so. 'I-I'm not your plaything!' She beat at him with her hands, and when she caught the mocking sparkle of his eyes she lost all control and slapped his jaw. He merely laughed low in his throat, but when she would have repeated the slap he suddenly stepped aside with the agility he had never lost, and Romy staggered and saved herself against the edge of his desk. Her hair flew in a wing half across her face, her green eyes blazed, and her body had the slim tenseness of the swords upon the wall ... those symbols of his ruthlessness.

There was silence, so absolute it was unnerving, and then the music started again ... *no hay amor como su amor* ... no love like this love.

'The wind has dropped,' he said. 'Perhaps it listens to the music.'

Romy fought not to look at him and stared at the two magnificent Goya paintings on the wall beyond his head, one of a woman in carnation red, the other of a matador in black and gold. The flesh tones were superb, the eyes were bold, the colours alive and glowing. Everything in this room was of the very best; he selected his possessions with the keen eye of a connoisseur ...

'What is it you want of me?' she demanded. 'A total submission before you let me go?'

'A total submission I would find tedious. No, *niña*, I enjoy our scuffles; they are like the pinch of spice on the tortilla.'

'You are a devil a-and I won't be made fun of!' Romy struggled with the clasp of the bracelet, but it was firmly locked about her wrist, like the chain of a prisoner. 'Take these off me ... I don't want to wear them!'

'To take them off I shall have to come near you, *niña*, and you seem to find my proximity quite intolerable.'

She held out her arm and braced herself as he approached her with his silent tread. A shudder ran through her as his fingers touched her skin. He pressed a tiny concealed lock and the bracelet came undone, a chain of living green fire in his hand.

'These gems came originally from the jungle,' he said meaningly, and he let the bracelet drop to his desk. 'And now shall I remove the necklace before it chokes you?'

'Please.'

She turned her back to him, and then gave a little choked cry as he placed his hands around her throat and held her so that she felt the pressure of his fingers. 'You foolish child,' he mocked. 'In some ways you are not yet as grown up as Carmencita.'

He undid the necklace and released her. 'Go, run away to your bed and dream your little girl dreams.'

She walked to the door without looking back, aware that he stood and ran the emeralds through his fingers like drops of jungle fire ... the skin of her neck still felt the touch of both.

CHAPTER NINE

During the next few days Romy had no chance to be alone with Luis. The Don was making a tour of the region in order to speak with the farmers and to hear their troubles, and his friend rode with him. They would return late to the *hacienda*, tired and dusty, ready only for a cool shower, long glasses of *sangria*, and deep chairs in the shade of the patio trees.

The deep timbre of their voices, speaking in Spanish, would drift upwards to Romy's *mirador*, and secure behind its lacy iron she would listen to the sound and recognise that the two men valued each other's friendship in equal measure, and she grew uncertain of her plan of hoped-for freedom. She had no wish to turn the Don against Luis. All she wanted ...

Restless, undecided, she rode off alone the following day, not joining the other young people for their morning canter—an amusing procedure as a rule, with its cavalcade of children and ponies, the strumming guitars of the older boys, and Carmencita's bold glances at the Don's *gauchos*. Romy couldn't help but wonder what the girl's reaction would be if one of them should accept the invitation of her eyes and snatch her from the saddle. They looked capable of it, with their sun-bitten faces, wide hats shading wicked eyes, and colourful shirts.

The morning was a warm mingling of sun and blue sky; of pampas grass and prickly pear, shaped more oddly than any other plant on earth, its knobbly fingers pointing in aimless directions.

Romy made for the adobe village across the lake, where she could stable her horse for a few *pesetas* and wander in the market place. Odd and charming mementoes could be bought quite cheaply, and lunch could be made of baked sweet potatoes at a stall, and fruit bought from a pannier and eaten in the shade of an adobe wall. Papaya, plums, and custard apples ...

The siesta dream of a tourist again, her troubles held at bay for a while.

Dressed *de corto*, with her hair pinned beneath her riding hat, and wearing a shirt and narrow riding trousers, Romy felt and looked rather like a boy. She almost wished she were a boy, with the freedom to ride away, perhaps, on a Mexican truck heading for the border, without the fear of being discovered as a girl; green-eyed, fair hair spilling from the Cordoban hat, at the mercy of a man who was not an *hidalgo*.

She shivered and gave Duquesa her lump of sugar before leaving her at the stables. The mare whinnied as if to warn her that they should be making for home, but Romy soothed her and told her in Spanish not to fuss. 'The *dueno* is miles away, my angel, and today is mine to do with as I wish. Now eat your sugar and enjoy the shade out of the sun.'

The morning passed almost before Romy knew it, so engrossed did she become in the intricate lay-out of the village, where each narrow street led eventually to the colour and noise and spiciness of the market place. Some of the women wore the regional costume, a vermilion or black skirt banded with contrasting colour, with slitted sleeves to the jacket to show a lace blouse. Dark oiled hair was plaited into fine chain-like braids coiled at the nape of the neck. Earrings swung provocatively against copper skin, and sloping eyes held centuries of mystery and passion, and now and then a glimpse of rebellion.

Her own feeling of rebellion was like a distant thunder in her blood, there but no longer holding her in a tense grip. The spell of this place had worked its magic and she was lost in the goods piled in a heap, desirous of owning a delicate lace *mantilla* which in England could be used as a scarf at the neck of her scarlet raincoat.

Strange that she had left her raincoat behind, as if in Mexico it never rained. She smiled, and then caught back the smile with biting teeth. Because of the rain ... ah, it had poured from the heavens that night!

'The *señorito* likes, eh?'

The voice of the vendor recalled her. 'Quite well ... how much are you asking, *señor*?'

They bargained and the *mantilla* became Romy's. As she folded it and put it in her pocket she had to grin to herself. A *senorito* was a young man, and the vendor no doubt thought that the *mantilla* was a gift for a flashing-eyed *chiquita*.

Romy sauntered, acting the boy. Had she the courage to run away, now? There was a mule-cart ... but where was the driver? She looked around and became aware that the market place was becoming deserted. Shutters were closing, the time of siesta was at hand, and it would take far more cash than she carried to persuade the driver of the cart to abandon his rest while the hot sun took possession of the day.

Romy made for an old courtyard near the church and made herself comfortable on a wooden seat bowed over by a plumbago tree. She tilted her hat as she had seen the *gauchos* do, not to mention the Don himself. Darn him, intruding upon her thoughts and bedevilling her! She closed her eyes tightly, but there was his face, so vivid that she had to let her eyelids fly open so that she might be certain that he had not appeared in all his height and darkness, there against the sun, looking down at her with those mocking bronze eyes.

No, she was quite alone but for the *reinitas*, tiny birds that flew about with a shy twittering, searching for honey and pretty as paint. Little queens, perhaps the same ones who came to the patio each morning to take jam and sugar from the bird table.

Why could she never escape even in her thoughts from her graceful prison? Yes, the *hacienda* was a place of beauty and grace, roofed over with its mellow old tiles and great clusters of flowering vine, planted centuries ago by the first Avarado, a captain of conquest from Spain, intent upon making his home as Spanish as possible. Luscious wine-coloured oleanders framed the family chapel, where the Don's ancestor had been married to the girl who had travelled by ship to a strange land and an unknown bridegroom.

So were matters arranged then, and even today. The Latin temperament seemed attuned to the conquest of a stranger ... the Don had said that love was just a pretty word used to express affection for a pet or a song or a favourite garment, and looking back to Lovtanet Bay she knew without a doubt that the few forlorn tears she had shed on the beach, standing there in her bridesmaid dress, had been tears of disillusion. She had not run away because of a broken heart ... she had left Bristol without giving Lance a thought ... when she tried to recall his face she could hardly do so, yet she had known him from childhood.

Life was certainly full of surprises, and she reached up to fondle a spray of plumbago and felt a sudden sharp sting as a wasp buzzed and flew off. Romy looked at her hand and saw the red mark of the sting ... the asp in the garden, she thought wryly, and decided it was time to fetch her stabled horse and ride back to the *hacienda*.

She strolled the deserted streets, nursing her stung hand as she passed the adobe houses with rough white walls hung with pots of plants and painted saints in the little niches. She walked beneath limewashed archways and was glad of the shade after the heat of the sun. A dog stirred against a wall and scratched lazily. A snatch of *quichua*, the Indian dialect, stole from a window. It made Romy very aware of the strangeness of the place, of dark eyes watching her from behind a curtain as she passed by.

She arrived at the stables and entered, breathing the tang of horses and hay. She made for the stall in which she had left Duquesa, only to find it empty! She stared and felt a stab of alarm. Hastily she glanced in the other stalls, none of which held the proud and glossy young mare, whose bridle was bright and polished, and whose pedigree was apparent at a glance.

Suddenly frightened, Romy ran to the shabby little office where she had paid her *pesetas* to have Duquesa minded for a few hours. The boy was sleeping and as she shook him awake his straw hat slipped from his head to reveal his startled face. With very little Spanish at her command Romy could only make him understand that her horse was missing by dragging him to the stall which she had rented. 'Look, my horse is gone! Duquesa, the mare I ride at the wish of Don Delgado, the *dueno* of the *valle*. Do you understand me?'

He understood who the Don was and comprehended that the horse was missing, and at once the boy broke into a spate of Spanish and looked as scared as Romy. She didn't want to believe what had obviously happened ... while the stable boy took his siesta someone had entered the stable and stolen the best horse in the place. '*Mierda!*' the boy groaned. '*Ay Dios mio!*'

Romy sank down on a mounting stone and pulled off her hat to fan her hot yet blanched face. Her hair tumbled about her shoulders and the boy stared at her. '*Una señorita!*' he exclaimed, and looked at her trousers and back again at her face framed by the tawny hair. If the situation had not been so serious Romy might have laughed at the boy's expression.

'What do we do, *chico*? Is there a police station ...' She sought for the Spanish words and made him understand, but he shook his head. The *pueblo* was too small for a station of the law.

'Then who ...?'

'*El padre.*' The boy grabbed her hand. '*Pronto, por favor.*'

Together they hastened down the street to the house of the local priest, and Romy prayed that he could speak English and be able to do something to help. The Don would flay her for having left Duquesa to be stolen ... but she hadn't dreamed such a thing would happen. She had visited the village before ... yes, but in the company of Luis and Tio Isidro! It made all the difference, darn it. They belonged, but she was obviously a foreigner, and presumed to be rash and foolish. Why not steal her horse, if she was thoughtless enough to leave such a fine animal in the local stable?

She and the Mexican boy arrived breathlessly at the old door set in a high wall, with a small iron judas through which the boy peered. *'Padre,'* he called through the little grille. *'Señor Cura, uno momento, por favor!'*

Romy guessed from the boy's expressive shrug that the Father was taking his siesta and they were disturbing the ritual. All the same the door was opened and there stood a sun-weathered figure in a black cassock and a straw hat. 'Carlos?' he exclaimed. *'Que ocurre, chico? Que hay?'*

The boy explained very rapidly what had happened, with gestures of heartfelt innocence.

'Dios mio!' The Father stared at Romy, then swept off his straw hat. 'Good day to you, *señorita*. The boy tells me you are an Americano visitor to the *pueblo* and that your mount has been taken from the stable where he works? This is so?'

'Yes, Father, except that I am English.' Romy was relieved almost to the point of tears to find that someone in this forsaken place spoke a language she could understand. 'I am staying at the Hacienda del Valle and I came here today on a very fine mare owned by the Don. When I returned to the stable in order to collect my mount, she was no longer there. The animal is valuable, Father, and the stable boy tells me there is no *comisaria* in the village. Please, can you help me?'

'First, *señorita*, you must come into my garden and take a chair. You are out of breath from walking too fast in the heat ... come sit down and I will arrange for a message to be sent to the *hacienda*.'

'Oh, but ...' Alarm caught at Romy's heart like cold fingers. 'Can't we make enquiries first, before informing the Don that Duquesa is missing? I mean, she might only have been borrowed by someone for a ride. The person might return her, and those at the *hacienda* will be worried unduly.'

'I can see that you are worried, *señorita*.' The good Father's eyes dwelt with a glimmer of shrewdness upon her anxious face. 'Very well, I will send my servant Carlos to make enquiries, but if the mare is still unreturned by Angelus, then the Señor Don Delgado must be told. He will contact the *guardia* by telephone. I am not connected, you see.'

'You're very kind.' Romy smiled and breathed again. There was still hope that Duquesa would be found before it became necessary to inform the Don ... she dreaded his anger, the very thought of it made her legs go so weak that she was thankful to sit down in a fan-backed chair while Father Sabio, as the Mexican boy called him, went into his house to fetch his servant Carlos.

She smiled at the boy who still hovered by the door in which the judas window was set like a rather malevolent eye. He still looked rather scared, as if she might blame him for the theft, or the borrowing of the Don's valuable horse, but Romy could only blame herself. She had come here alone when she should have stayed with Carmencita and the others, and her impulse had as usual led to trouble.

Trouble had seemed to lurk at her shoulder ever since her advent into Mexico ... the eye of the Devil as the Don had called it, following her around and no doubt grinning wickedly when she walked into yet another spot of bother.

Carlos and the boy departed, and Father Sabio brought a jug of wine to the table set beside the woven-cane chairs in the shade of an old lime tree.

'You will take a glass of wine, *señorita*?'

She hesitated, and then decided that she needed something to steady her shaken nerves. 'Please.'

He sat down in the other chair and poured the wine. 'I can see that you need a little consolation after your shock. This is made locally and the wine treaders always present me with a few bottles for my cellar. It is rather a nice colour, eh? Like a topaz.'

She smiled, grateful for the wine before the questions. Also she had hurried through the assaulting sun of this semi-tropical *pueblo* and the wine was refreshing.

'Will you permit that I smoke my pipe, *señorita*?'

'Of course, Father.' She watched as he lit the carved old pipe and puffed the strong tobacco. She suspected that he knew a little more about her than the villagers; they had not met before, but he had no doubt guessed that she was the English girl the Don was rumoured to be marrying. He must therefore think it strange that she should be in fear of the man she was supposed to love ... or did it seem perfectly natural to him? A natural part of Latin courtship that a Spaniard should give his *novia* a silver-bridled horse to ride, and set her quaking when the horse went astray?

'You have heard of me, haven't you, Father?'

'Yes. I had heard there was a fair-haired young woman at the house of the Don. I guessed when I saw you ... but I am perplexed that you are so many miles from the *hacienda* and all alone. It is not ...'

'Proper?' she murmured.

'But you are English, so of course ...'

'I do improper things.'

He puffed his pipe and watched from beneath tufted brows as her fingers played restlessly with the wine glass. 'I am not too old, nor too rigid in my views, not to understand the follies of the young. In any case, human beings are inexplicable, impulsive, and predestined.'

'You Latins are all such fatalists, Father!'

'Why not, child? If you had not come riding this way today, then your horse would not be missing and you would not be wondering nervously how your *novio* will react.' Father Sabio's smile was quizzical. 'He is known to have a temper to match his generosity.'

'He sets great store by the mare.' Romy gave a little shiver as she grew cooler in the shade of the lime tree and the sky began to take that deeper shade of blue as the afternoon waned. 'You wouldn't think it of a once famous matador that he should care so much for an animal.'

'Do you regard the matador as heartless?'

'Nerveless.' Her smile was shaky. 'You have an attractive walled garden, Father. I have never seen camellias so huge and velvety, not even in the gardens at the *hacienda*. You must have green fingers.'

'I like to grow things.' He arose and cut a pair of the lovely flowers growing on a single stem. He gave them to Romy with that touch of gallantry so disarming in the Latin male.

'*Gracias.*' She caressed the petals and wished she might hide away in this walled garden, but that would be cowardly. an admission that she feared to face the Don and his famous temper. What would he do? Her heart seemed to turn over. Would he be angry enough to set her free? It was what she wanted, yet not at the expense of Duquesa, whom he had trusted her to take care of.

'You have hurt your hand, *señorita*?' Father Sabio had taken hold of her hand and was examining the swelling on the back of it. 'Ah, this is a sting and it needs a little soda to take down the swelling and ease the irritation. I will fetch some.'

'You're very kind ...'

'I am pleased that in this matter I can help, child. I am not so sure about the mare. On market days we have all sorts in and out of the village and it may not be in my power to ... anyway, we will hope for the best, but if Carlos returns empty-handed ...' Father Sabino raised his own hands expressively, and then went indoors to fetch the soda.

Romy, all on edge, began to walk about the garden, which was full of birds, scarlet-tailed, others yellow-breasted with bright pink beaks, and a macaw that swept a branch with a long blue tail. At any other time Romy would have found delight in this old-world place, but the time was passing and she truly dreaded the moment when the Don came striding through that door, looking like thunder and ready to shake the breath out of her. She sank down on the coping of a fish pond and wrapped her arms about herself like a bird folding its frightened wings. A breeze stirred through the trees, rippled the water where the fish lurked red and gold, and played over Romy's bare arms in the thin silk shirt.

After bringing the soda for her hand Father Sabio had to leave for the evening service at the little church. Carlos returned with very little information beyond that a woman had heard during siesta the sound of hooves beneath her window and the jingle of a bridle. That would have been about three o'clock, a short time before Romy had returned to the stable to find Duquesa gone.

'I must now send a message to Don Delgado,' the Father said, firmly but kindly. 'Are you so afraid of him, child?'

'I ... I seem always to do the wrong thing, Father. I'm impulsive and it makes him mad.'

'No one human is angelic, and perhaps you expect it of him, to be a saint when instead he is very

154

much a man and a Spaniard into the bargain.'

'How he is a Spaniard!' She had to smile as she doctored her sting with the soda. 'And I am English, and never the twain shall fully understand each other.'

'You may find, my child, that we Latins are attuned to the fact that women suffer in mysterious ways and seem almost to enjoy it.'

'Father!' She gave him a rather shocked look. 'How can you say that we enjoy being hurt?'

'When we are hurt, and when we are happy, we are more aware than at any other time of being fully alive. Women are by nature more sensitive and by reason of that they feel everything with more intensity. And now I will leave you in the good care of Carlos, who will cook you a meal and ensure that you have all you need.'

When the garden door closed behind the kindly figure of Father Sabio, a moth flew in and hovered on the edge of the wall. Romy saw plainly the flame cross and impression of a skull on the black body, and in her highly strung mood it seemed like a symbol of the encounter she must face later on.

Carlos served a delicious meal of baked rabbit, tomatoes, onions, and peppers, but Romy could not do it justice, though she drank several cups of coffee and made herself more nervous than ever.

She sat alone in the Father's old-fashioned parlour, with its Mexican cushions and mats, and mixture of cane and mahogany furniture. There were books and among them a copy of *David*

Copperfield. She tried to lose herself in the book, but each time the clock chimed the quarter hour, she felt her heart skip a beat.

By now they would know at the *hacienda* where she was, and soon someone would arrive to take her back to face the dueno's wrath. From the porch leading out to the garden she watched the sun burn out of the sky and heard the sound of the Angelus bell drifting along the quiet, darkening streets. Coppery golden clouds hung in the sky, and then the garden turned slowly to a place of shadows, and everything was still and waiting, and Romy was plucking the petals from her camellias without being aware of what she was doing.

The petals fell soundless to the ground, in front of the stone Virgin in chains ... and in the stillness came the soft whine of car wheels stopping in front of the house. The door had been left ajar for the caller to come in and fetch her. 'Here goes!' she thought, and finding her hands empty she plunged them into the pockets of her trousers and walked down the garden path to meet the driver of the car.

CHAPTER TEN

Their eyes clashed in the beam of the headlamps and Romy, already taut with nerves, was certain she would cry out if he touched her. She had hoped that having been busy all day he would send someone else for her, but here he was, punishing her with his presence even before he spoke a word to her.

She stood there as if enclosed in a bell-glass and the silence was deep and crushing as she waited for him to catechize her. He confronted her, dark and tall and ineffably the master of the situation, just as he had been on the train when he had insisted that she go home with him because scandal was something he would not tolerate.

It seemed as if an eternity rushed by before he turned and reached into the car for something. From the start Romy gave he might have been reaching for his whip.

'I-I'm hopelessly to blame for what happened,' she said shakily. 'It was entirely my fault ... I wanted to explore the *pueblo*, which took my fancy when Luis brought me here last week, and I left Duquesa at the local stable as if she were any ordinary horse. I'm sorry, I truly am ... and I deserve a scolding.'

'You deserve a spanking,' he drawled, 'and you would receive it, if Duquesa had not come home by herself, dragging her reins and thirsty but otherwise all right. Her pedigree cannot be hurt by how many miles she travels, only by neglect or misuse. You neglected to unsaddle the mare!'

Romy stared at him, then weak with relief she sank against the bonnet of the car. 'Thank heaven! I've been so worried ... so afraid.'

'Of me?' He raised slowly a black eyebrow and

deliberately took a step nearer to her.

'Y-yes.' She pressed herself against the steel body of the car and wondered in panic what form his punishment would take for even allowing his fine mare to be left in the hands of a Mexican stable boy. She had left the boy to unsaddle Duquesa, so eager had she been to lose herself and her troubled thoughts in the colourful market place. She had paid for the mare to be made comfortable ... no, there was no excuse for what she had done! Duquesa could so easily have been stolen! She deserved that glitter in the Don's eyes, and even as she shrank from him she submitted to his hands as they reached for her. Perhaps it was true what Father Sabino had said ... that women enjoyed their suffering.

Yet as his hands touched her, she looked thin, elfin, almost a slip of a boy in the car lights that cut in two the shadows all around them. The rate of her pulse beat was no secret to him as his fingers brushed her throat, fastening about her the poncho he had taken from the car!

'There, now perhaps you will stop shaking.' His fingers brushed against the thin silk of her shirt. 'No wonder you women go in fear of men when you dress like this!'

'I ... I dressed like this to ride in the sun ...'

'Without a hat?'

'Oh ... I must have left it in the Father's house.'

'I will fetch it. Get into the car and wait for me.'

Romy did as she was told, huddling down into

the warm folds of the woollen poncho, and still trembling a little from the shock of seeing him. It was such a relief that Duquesa was safe, but Romy was sure he wouldn't let her off with only a few words of disapproval. He was biding his time, awaiting his moment to take her unaware, and when she heard him returning to the car she kept her gaze fixed on the glimmer of the dashboard. He joined her inside the car and tossed her hat into the back. He slammed the door, started the engine, and backed along the lane that led into the main artery of the *pueblo*. The car became warm as the engine responded swiftly to his expert touch, and soon they were driving across the *sabana*, along the road that led inevitably to the *hacienda*.

'I am glad that you had the sense to go to Father Sabio,' he said after a suspenseful silence.

'You don't imagine I'd have tried walking to the *hacienda*?' She shot him a look and saw that his profile was stern and aloof in the down-reflecting roof light. She could tell that he was holding on to his temper, but she hadn't asked him to drive all this way to fetch her. He could have sent his chauffeur!

'I imagine you might have taken it into your head to find someone to take you in the opposite direction.'

'I hadn't enough money on me, nor did I fancy ...'

'What, *chica*?' His drawl softened meaningly. 'A tussle with an importunate Mexican? It could well

159

happen, dressed as you are.'

'I ... I was taken for a boy in the market place, and believe me I was tempted to beg a lift on a mule cart ... anything to get away from you!'

'You had Duquesa at your disposal, before you left her to wander home on her own.'

'The mare is yours, *señor*. I wouldn't steal her, and you are well aware that I don't know the country well enough to find my way to Xerica without getting hopelessly lost.'

'Xerica, with its airport of departure for England and home, eh? Shall I drive you there right now, put you on a plane, and be rid of you?'

She couldn't take her eyes from his face. 'Would you do that? No, I can see you are mocking me, playing one of your subtle games, building up my hopes only to knock them down!'

'How well you know me, but women are intuitive, are they not, about men and their motives?'

'Your sarcasm is intolerable. I knew the moment I saw you tonight that you had it in for me. You just can't resist taunting me for proving once again what an incompetent creature I am in comparison to the incomparable Latin girl. I need the keeper, in your opinion. I'm hopeless without one.'

'A mere child, less capable than the mare I trained myself to always find her way home.'

'Naturally! What is yours must have the homing instinct ... but I'm no pigeon.'

'I agree, *chica*. You are more of a goose.'

'The goose has been known to outfly the arrogant eagle!'

'But not to outwit him.'

'We'll see, *señor*.' Romy sat as far away as possible from him, wrapped in the poncho she would have been grateful for, had he not been so unbearable ... and male ... calling her a child and a goose!

Suddenly he laughed, and that too whipped at her outraged nerves. She felt the colour rise hot to her temples and she gave way to temper. 'I wish it had been Luis who came for me,' she said hotly. 'He has a better nature than you, a-and feelings more human than those you exhibit. He would realise how miserable and upset I've been, all these hours, and try to be a little kinder than you can stoop to manage.'

'You want a demonstration of ... kindness?' In an instant the brakes were applied and the car sped to a halt in the very centre of the bridge that spanned the lake. There they hovered above the sheerest drop, the waters of the lake spread beneath them, deep and dark as the Spanish eyes that drowned out all the world as Romy was caught in the Don's arms and his lips crushed the cry that broke from her. His arms and the poncho imprisoned her; she was helpless to resist the onslaught of his kisses. They were everywhere, blinding her eyes, warm against the hollow of her throat, there at her earlobes, a relentless invasion of senses she had not known she possessed.

'No!' She tried to turn her head away, but his

hand caught and held in the tawny tangle of her hair so that it hurt if she twisted away from him. He was whispering words which she sensed to be Spanish love words, and fear grew in her that she would not escape this time from what had threatened on the roof of the *atalaya*.

'Gado ... please ...'

He became instantly still, holding her within the curve of a steel-like arm, his other hand lost in the silk of her hair, so that she could not escape his gaze upon her red lips, her green eyes, her white skin.

'Don't,' she pleaded. 'Don't always blame me for what happened that night on the train. I didn't make the rain, or the breakdown. I didn't cast a spell so you would walk into my sleeping compartment by mistake. I ... I wish with all my heart I had never come to Mexico ... the place causes only trouble for me and I don't want more of it.'

Tears had come into her eyes and now they spilled and ran down her cheeks. 'Let me go away, then when everyone has forgotten that I ever came to the valley, you can marry Carmencita.'

'I don't take orders from a woman.' He bent his head and his lips brushed the tears from her face. 'I am far too much the tyrant, as you would say, to release you from my life. We are going to be married, no matter what you say.'

'Y-you can't force me to marry you. I won't, just for the sake of a scandal that never was!'

'What if there is a scandal, a real one, *chica*? I hold you at my mercy. I could do anything I pleased with you. If you tried to open that door beside you, you would fall into the lake. I should feel compelled to dive in after you and the centre of the lake is so deep that we should both be drowned. Immortal lovers, *niña*. Does it not sound romantic?'

'It sounds crazy. Gado ... I mean, *señor*, be reasonable.'

'I am being perfectly reasonable. I brought you to the *hacienda* to marry you, and that is what I intend to do.'

'But it was all ... fake. People only marry when they love each other.' She moved tentatively and at once his arm tightened into a curve of captivity. 'Y-you know I hate you.'

'It will be my pleasure to teach you how to do the opposite.'

'That's typical of your arrogance,' she said stormily. 'But you'd be wasting your time. A pupil can't be taught something she is unwilling to learn, no matter how expert the teacher ... and I am sure you are an expert, having been an idolised matador. They are, I believe, notorious for their *amors* with every pretty *señorita* who throws them a rose.'

'You make dangerously provoking remarks, *niña*, and let me remind you again that we are very much alone and having been an *espada* I am also ruthless.' He spoke the word against her ear. 'You consider me very ruthless, don't you? So what have I to lose if I teach you a lesson in love, here and now?'

'Love?' She hoped the scorn in her voice hid the tremor she could not control. 'My ideas of love are about as much like yours as ... as the sun is to the moon.'

'Really? Don't you know that in our mythology the sun and the moon are lovers?'

'They would be, in your mythology! Especially as your southern sun is an assault rather than a caress.'

'Do you then regard love as a thing of tender caresses and whispered endearments?'

'I ... I should hope it isn't as savage as your sun can be.' She sat rigid within the circle of his arm, and hoped that while they argued he would not kiss her again so closely that each bone in her body, each nerve and limb seemed to vibrate unbearably, almost to the point of pain, so that she had come close to moaning in his arms. He would like that. It was in his nature to enjoy being cruel to her.

'The soft and tender things are never as exciting, *niña*, as the more primitive things. The hard-shelled passion fruit is more delicious than the peach once the shell is cracked. The dragonfly that eats the moth is gorgeous. The Moors who ruled with the sword made gardens like jewels. The cactus, which we call the cruel flower, holds water for the man lost in the desert. Life, you know, would be fearfully dull if it were not enlivened by danger. If we knew what lay around every strange corner ... and what lay in the stranger's heart.'

He tilted her chin with an imperious finger and

forced her eyes to look into his, there in the intimate, shadowy light of the car, poised there on the bridge, like a wasp clinging to the rim of a water glass.

'If you were a girl who really liked everything to be cosy and narrow you would not have spent your grandmother's legacy on a journey to Mexico. And alone, *niña*!'

'That really tries your temper, doesn't it, *señor*? It's at the root of every argument we have. Your Spanish colonial nature just can't tolerate the thought of a woman being able to look after herself.'

'Can you?' He quirked an eyebrow in the mocking way she found so infuriating. 'You gaze at the world with such wide and innocent eyes, don't you? A babe in the jungle. Hardly aware yet of what life is all about, and why men and women find each other so exciting. It was your eyes I noticed that day in Mexico City. Green eyes for danger, and the earth shook. Then the rains came, and an angel or a devil's hand led me into your sleeping compartment.'

'I-I'm sure it was the devil's,' Romy said, defying him with the green eyes he had likened to the Avarado bride gems. At once his arms tightened and she felt the strength that could have crushed her body as his strength of will had crushed her resistance on the train. Now if she resisted he would kiss her with those kisses that whirled her around until she couldn't think straight, until the danger made her submit to a marriage that would leave his pride unblemished and his ambitions untouched by the breath of scandal.

Feminine instinct came to her rescue and she let herself go slack in his arms, allowed her eyes to close as if she might faint.

'Romola?' His breath stirred warm against her eyelids. 'Poor child, you look worn out, a waif of the night, in the hands of a devil you don't much like.'

Those same hands laid her back against the seat, and a moment later she felt the throbbing of the engine. The car moved on across the bridge, and the sardonic irony of his words kept revolving in her mind. A man such as the Don could never love what he called 'a waif of the night'. She, that waif, would never marry him, no matter what he did, or said, or submitted her to. She had her pride and it rejected a marriage of convenience, one that would grow roots of resentment and bear the bitter fruit of regret when he became Ambassador and his lady could not look a Latin, or behave like one. Beautiful, submissive, yet fiery beneath it all.

All the lamps in their iron sconces were alight in the courtyard and along the veranda, and members of the family were gathered in groups to await the arrival of Don Delgado with his truant *novia*. When the car came to a halt they milled around it, and it was into the arms of Luis that Romy stumbled. He looked into her eyes, read their message of imploration and assisted her into the house with a firmness that held at bay the solicitous but curious aunts. 'I just want to go to my room, Luis. I'm so

166

weary ...'

Somehow she achieved her wish and when at last she was alone she sank across the smoothness of her bed and let her body relax at last from the tension of the past hours. Ah, it felt so good to be here, with the turbulent events of the day behind her at last, and she was almost drifting off to sleep when the beany spiciness of fresh-made coffee stole to her nostrils.

She had not heard the door open, but when she turned her head she saw Doña Dolores standing beside her bed. Romy sat up and pressed the tumbled hair away from her eyes. She had no idea how defenceless she looked; how much the stranger in the enormous Spanish bed.

'Poor child, you have had a worrying time, Delgado tells me. Let me pour you a cup of coffee, and later on when you have rested you may have a supper tray here in your room.'

'That would be nice, *señora*, though I could come down if you prefer ...?'

'Not at all.' A cup of delicious coffee was handed to Romy, made from the beans grown in the valley. To her surprise as she sipped it, Doña Dolores sat down on the foot of her bed. Her dark eyes studied the pale contours of Romy's face, around which her tawny hair was clouded. Her slender hand played with the antique pendant which hung against the silk of her dress.

'When the mare returned riderless we were all very worried here at the *hacienda*. We thought you might have been thrown.'

Romy gazed at the woman who had every reason to wish that she and the Don had never crossed paths, and yet in her eyes there seemed a look of genuine concern. Romy longed to respond to it, but she dared not believe that the Don's mother felt any sympathy for her, the interloper into her home; the girl who had disrupted her plans regarding a union between Carmencita and her son: the bringing together of two of the oldest families in the region.

'I am sorry to have caused so much anxiety.' Romy's hands gripped her coffee cup, for this was not the time to say that soon the entire family would be rid of her; that none of them need fear that she meant to marry without being loved. Such an arrangement might suit a Latin girl, but Romy was far too sensitive to be able to face even the thought of a loveless possession.

'We have not spoken together very often, Romola, but I should like you to feel at home with us. I have noticed that you seem a little *soledad*, as we say. But that is only natural for a while. Our valley has an insidious way of stealing the heart, until it seems the only place to live. Years ago, before Gado was born, I was unhappy here. I was young and wilful ... would you believe that?'

Romy studied the woman who had borne a proud and wilful son; the silver at her temples, as if painted there. The expressive eyes; the mingling of tolerance in the beautiful woman, combined with certain shades of Latin intolerance. She had eloped with Delgado's father, and because the marriage had been a tempestuous one, she now believed firmly in the arranged union. It was understandable.

A smile softened the pensiveness of Romy's face. 'I suppose to be young is to be impulsive and on the brink of trouble a good deal of the time. You must have been very young when you married, *señora*.'

A soft flush stole into the smooth olive of the *señora*'s face and her eyes held for a moment the burning memory of the wild but unhappy love she had known with her husband. 'I was too young to know anything about men. Ramon had always had his own way, here in the wilds of Mexico, and I was accustomed to the constraints of the convent. Ramon came on a visit to southern Spain; he was buying bulls for his farm and my father bred the best. We met, we fell madly in love ... the girl just out of convent school, and the dashing *gaucho* who sprang from a long line of colonial Spaniards with a dash of Aztec blood in the veins. I knew that I was meant for a man selected by my father, much older than me and of a rather serious nature. I wanted Ramon and so I eloped with him to Mexico.'

The *señora*'s fingers clenched hard on the Spanish locket, and Romy couldn't help but wonder if it held a miniature of that wild young man she had been unable to resist.

'I left Ramon within six months of our marriage.

For a Latin girl to leave her husband is a serious matter ... that is why I must be sure that Delgado has not made the mistake of carrying off a girl just to satisfy an impulse.'

'But you know....' Romy's heart beat fast. 'It was a matter of expediency. He cannot afford a scandal in his position.'

'Has he ... made love to you?' The *señora*'s head was elegantly poised on her slender neck as she asked the question, but her eyes were pained, as if she didn't wish to hurt or embarrass Romy.

Romy thought of his kisses in the car, so deliberate and punishing, but knew it was not that kind of lovemaking to which his mother referred.

She shook her head, and heard a soft sigh of relief escape the *señora*'s lips. She rose to her feet, and her fingers relaxed their tense hold on the locket. 'I am glad we have talked, Romola. The atmosphere seems lighter between us. We are more *simpatica*.'

'Yes,' said Romy, but she looked young and uncertain curled up on the gold and scarlet bed. She wanted to say outright that the *señora* need have no more fear of another broken marriage in the family, but words alone would not convince her. It would take action. A deed of kind, such as the one which had brought her here.

A day alone with Luis on the mysterious lake island, to which the Indians never went, should jolt the pride which had made the Don bring her home with him. It should convince everyone that such a flighty miss should be sent away again.

'Xerica?' he had mocked. 'With its airport of departure for England and home?'

'Home,' she whispered, as the door of her bedroom closed behind the slender figure of Doña Dolores, and the night breezes stirred the flowering vine which had crept from the *mirador* right inside the room, alive and scented.

Her bedsitter would seem dull and austere after the colour and scent of her Spanish bedroom ... she would miss this old, fascinating, rambling house, its walks of delight, and the golden *sabana*, but in England she would be her own mistress again and not the masquerading *novia* of a man who put pride and position before anything else. She slipped off the bed and smoothed the cover, and as the silk whispered beneath her fingers she seemed to hear again the words spoken by Doña Dolores a moment before she had made her departure from the room. 'I want above all for Gado to know real happiness and not the passion that burns out leaving only bitterness in its place.'

Romy wandered out to her vine-shrouded *mirador* and found that a moon had risen and that the night held a mystery that breathed of elemental things. Don Delgado was his father's son also, and the same passions must stir his blood and smoulder in those bronze eyes until they seemed like the eyes of a furious, graceful animal.

His mother could not know how he looked at a girl until her very soul cried out for mercy. Such a man was like this half-pagan night and its moon like an Aztec shield.

If he took a woman without loving her ... Romy caught her breath and put a hand to her throat. Someone was pacing the courtyard below the enclosure in which she stood, cigar smoke arose on the still air, so strangely still since the moon had arisen, and Romy breathed the now familiar aroma of the Don's cigar.

Long and prowling were his strides from one side of the patio to the other, and when Romy peered from among the vines she could make out his tall figure in the rays of the moon. The black velvet of his smoking coat was like the pelt of a panther, to match the way he prowled the circular patio, almost as if it were a cage from which he sought some means of escape.

The pulse beneath her fingers seemed to throb more insistently. He desired escape as much as she did. Anger with the fates, a male reaching out for some prize or compensation, had made him insist that she marry him.

A marriage of convenience ... and angry passion!

Suddenly she felt his gaze upon her *mirador* and she stood as still as a bird among its foliage and prayed that his keen eyes would not see and assume that she was spying on him. She saw the dark tilt of his head in the moonlight, the smoke of his cigar rising against the pallor of the moonglow. Did he sense that she was there? Her heart seemed as if it were trying to beat its way out of her body, and then he turned away and a moment later she heard him speaking to someone. There was the lacy gleam of a pale mantilla, the glitter of earrings, and then a girlish laugh.

Carmencita had joined him in the patio. They seemed to stand very close together for several moments ... the girl's bracelet of tiny golden bells caught the moonlight as her arm curved upwards and encircled his neck. Romy held her breath, then she retreated into her room before she saw the completion of that embrace.

She had known that no man of the Don's age and temperament could treat Carmencita as if she were a niece. The girl was as glowing and warm as a carnation on a slender stem ... she was like the song she liked to sing to the music of her young brother's guitar. '*The woman is the chalice, the man is the wine.*'

She was made, as Doña Dolores knew, for a man like the *dueno*.

CHAPTER ELEVEN

THE Don's tour of inspection ended, after which he was kept busy in his study writing reports and letters. This was a relief for Romy. It meant she saw more of Luis, who seemed attuned to her mood, which was a mixture of gaiety and determination to return to her own way of life as soon as possible.

Then came a surprise ... Luis mentioned that the

Don had received a rather lengthy telegram from the Embassy in Mexico City, and that same evening the Don asked Romy to accompany him to his study because he wished to speak with her.

'I . . . was going to listen to the music, *señor*,' she said, hoping wildly that he would not insist.

His eyes insisted, warning her that he would take hold of her and march off with her in front of the family. With a little shrug, and a smile at Luis, she left the patio where the family were gathered for the evening and walked beside the Don to his sanctum. Her every nerve was tingling, and she had to fight to look composed when he opened the door of his study and ushered her into the room, with its leather floor-covering, its swords and capes, and aura of good cigars and a total lack of female influence.

He indicated that she sit down in one of the leather wing-backed chairs. 'A glass of wine might help you to relax,' he drawled, and he went to a carved cabinet and took from it a carafe of wine and a pair of stemmed glasses. As he poured the wine, Romy strove to look as if she didn't remember in vivid detail the last time they had been alone. She tilted her chin and watched his approach across the room, his features unsmiling, but his eyes so mockingly aware of her tension.

'To what shall we drink?' He handed her one of the glasses and seemed deliberately to let his fingers touch hers. Then he lounged against the high carved mantel, the family eagle above his head and in its talons the dove like a ruffled flower. 'To a journey without incident, shall we say?'

Romy stared at him. 'A journey, *señor?* Are you going away, or are you letting me go?'

'Which would you prefer?' He took a lazy sip at his wine. 'Come, don't spare my feelings.'

'Have you any?' she asked, more from defiance than a belief that he couldn't ache at heart or bleed when hurt. Looking at him in his dark suit, with the heavy silk shirt so white against the dark-gold skin, she could imagine the scar which he carried and the spell he had cast in the bullring. His fascination was the most dangerous thing about him, and clad in a fighting cape he would have quickened the heart of every woman who watched him stroll across the sand to match his quickness and subtlety against the temper and strength of a bull who faced for the first time a man who swung a coloured cape in its face.

No fighting bull was ever trained, being born a fighter. Up until its advent into the ring it was kept from any knowledge of flickering capes and the supple daring of a matador. At the *estáncias*, so Romy had been told by Tio Isidro, the aspiring *espadas* learned their tricks by fighting the heifers. It was the most courageous of the heifers who eventually gave birth to the brave bulls. The bulls were sacred, like Mithras, until their entrance into the arena ... their hour of glory, and the matador's moment of truth.

'You are giving me such a strange look, *niña.*

Drink your wine and I will tell you about our trip.'

'Our ... trip?' A sudden terror gripped her. What could he possibly mean ... a honeymoon?

'You look on the verge of a swoon ... please to drink your wine before I have to revive you with the kiss of life.'

'Don't you dare!' She swallowed half the wine in a gulp, and then looked at him with defiant eyes, the contours of her face revealed by the way her hair was clipped back in a silver buckle. Just as her eyes dominated her face, so did the leather chair dominate her slim figure.

'Do you now feel brave enough to hear the details of the trip?'

'Stop behaving as if this were a *corrida*. It isn't fair!'

'Stop looking at me as if I carry an invisible whip. It isn't very flattering.'

'I'm not a Latin girl, so I wouldn't know how to flatter a man.'

'No,' his eyes flicked her green-clad figure in the winged chair, 'you are certainly in no way a Latin girl. It should cause quite a lot of comment at the Embassy.'

'What do you mean? Oh, for heaven's sake stop playing verbal chess with me and tell me why you dragged me away from the music and why you keep talking about a trip. What trip?'

'The one you will be taking with Luis and myself to Mexico City.' He strolled to his desk and picked up a sheet of paper overlaid by the strips of a telegram. 'There is at this time of the year a carnival in the city and a ball to round off the saturnalia. I am requested to return to the Embassy to attend the ball and to meet various officials from Madrid. I am asked to be accompanied by my fiancée.'

Romy couldn't take her eyes from him, and then to give herself courage she finished her wine. 'I gather from what you say, *señor*, that you are expecting soon to be addressed as Your Excellency? I take it that I am to be inspected to make sure you are choosing the right wife for such an eminent position? How will you explain things when I return to England ... because I intend to return! I won't be sacrificed on the altar of your ambitions!'

She jumped to her feet as she spoke and ran to the door. With long supple strides he was there before her and blocking the way with his height and his relentless eyes.

'You will come to Mexico City and you will behave as my fiancée. If you attempt to run away I shall come after you and then you will learn how angry I can be when I have real cause to be so.'

'Ever since we met you have been making threats,' she stormed. 'Is that all you are capable of, even with Carmencita?'

'Why mention Carmencita?'

'Because she is the one you should take to meet your Spanish officials. She is the girl you ought to marry.'

'When the time arrives I shall marry whom I

choose to marry, but right now I am concerned with the carnival ball. You will attend it with me and I refuse absolutely to accept your refusal to do so ... do you hear me?'

Romy heard the pounding of her heart, and outside in the patio the strumming of guitars. There was no music more evocative than Latin music; no eyes in the world more expressive than Spanish eyes. The Don held her with his gaze, and unable to bear it a moment longer she turned away from him and went to study the Goya painting of the woman in a red frilled dress, holding in her hand a lacy fan above which her vivid eyes flirted with whoever looked at her.

'We endure some things so we may enjoy others.' The Don came and stood behind Romy, whose body tensed like one of those slender swords on the wall. 'Think of all those museums, not to mention the masked ball. Surely every young woman should attend one just once in her life.'

'You seem always to be making demands of me ... if I come to Mexico City will you make me a promise?'

'I must know the promise before I commit myself to keeping it.'

'Don't ... force me to marry you.'

He was silent for about half a minute, during which time Romy was acutely conscious of his supple figure behind her, and those arms that might suddenly enclose her in an embrace that mocked her fragile inability to escape from him. 'Very well,

Romola, I swear not to force you to become my wife. I will allow your emotions to dictate their own demands and desires, and having made this oath I shan't break it.'

'I should never forgive you if you broke such an oath, *señor*.'

'Turn, *niña*, and look into my eyes. They have, you know, a truth of their very own.'

She turned slowly and let her gaze dwell on his face. He looked almost stern as he gazed down at her, and slowly her hands relaxed their grip on each other. 'It wouldn't be right, *señor*, for two people to marry without ... love.'

'I agree ... and will you make me a promise?'

'Not to run away from my supposed lord and master?'

He took note of the smile that touched her lips. 'For that I demand a forfeit. Since our first meeting I have wanted to see the effect of one of my *chaquetas* against your skin and hair. Will you oblige?'

He reached for one of the matador short coats that hung upon the wall. 'This I wore as a youth of seventeen. Come, try it on.'

'To make our *corrida* seem more real?' she asked daringly.

He held the coat and after a slight hesitation she slipped her arms into the sleeves and was surprised to find that the gold and silver stitchings made it seem like a coat of mail. It gleamed against her green dress and her tawny hair, and made the Don narrow his eyes to study the effect.

'Do I look like a youth, *señor*?'

'Are you wishing you were, *chica*?'

'Sometimes with you it would be an advantage!'

He smiled with his eyes, until they seemed to hold fire. 'Perhaps we could then have been friends, eh? But you are most fetching in the *chaqueta*. Far more so than any youth.'

'Then if you don't mind I'll take it off.' She did so and handed it to him. He returned it to its place among his mementoes and Romy noticed the suggestive rent in the side of another jacket, and when she flashed an enquiring look at the Don he quirked an eyebrow and touched his side. 'Yes, my retribution for my sins,' he drawled. 'We go to the city on Thursday morning, by aeroplane from Xerica.'

'Y-you have no heart.' Her legs held the most curious tremor as she walked to his desk and touched the ornament which he used as a paperweight, a carved hand holding an uncut topaz, barbaric and yet at the same time strangely beautiful.

'I have certain duties and I intend to carry them out.'

She dared not look at him and kept her gaze on the hand stabbed by the gleaming stone. His tone of voice was explicit, he intended to have his way and she was left defenceless.

'I am glad that Luis is going with us,' she said.

'You like him, don't you?'

'Yes, very much.'

'Much more than you like me, eh?'

'Yes, do you mind?'

'If I minded would I give you this? Catch!'

To her own surprise she caught the object which he took from his pocket and tossed so carelessly. She looked at it as if it might burn her and heard him laugh softly and mockingly. 'It has nothing to do with the bride gems you took such a dislike to. It is designed in the tradition of the Incas.'

It was a wide bracelet of patterned gold. 'It's very lovely,' she said. 'I ... I will accept it, if there are no strings attached.'

'Do you see any?' he drawled.

'No ...' She slipped the bracelet over her fingers and felt its golden weight against the bones of her wrist. She would dismiss from her mind how much it had cost and enjoy without asking questions its pagan beauty. 'Thank you, *señor*.'

'You are welcome, *señorita*.' He seemed to mock the formality of her tone of voice.

'May I now join the others?' The weight of his bracelet against her wrist made her feel defenceless and defiant. It was a charming token, his way of saying *gracias* because he had made her promise to carry on with the masquerade until he was ready to ring down the curtain. Always he must have *his* way.

'By all means join those on the patio.' He gave her a faintly sardonic bow, and this time she was allowed to leave the study. Her legs still felt strangely shaky as she made for the patio, where the young people were dancing the *sevillana* with

181

gaiety and exuberance. Carmencita seemed to be on fire as she tapped her scarlet heels and whirled her skirts, and Romy was suddenly wild with the man who played with both of them as if they were mere dolls for his amusement. She found Luis and drew him to one side. 'Will you take me to the island tomorrow?' she asked. 'The Don is infuriating ... he's putting his career before everything ... everyone ... and I won't be a party to it!'

'The island?' Luis murmured. 'You seem drawn to it.'

'Yes, I want to see it, and this may be my last chance.'

'You want Gado to believe ...' Luis frowned and gazed over towards the dancing couples. Romy hung on to his answer. It was true about the island, as if some pagan voice called her to it, and there all her problems could be solved and answered.

Then Luis looked at her, just as the Don came out to watch the dancing. They were both acutely aware of that tall figure in the lamplight as Luis inclined his head and said with his eyes that he would take her to the island. He was not happy about it, but Romy felt a sense of elation as she fingered the Inca bracelet with its raised figures of sun, moon, and stars, and profiles which had the look of fierce pride and domination displayed by Don Delgado as he stood talking to his mother. Suddenly he took her slender hand and bent his head to kiss it. She touched his black hair with a gesture of infinite affection, reminding Romy of her words the other night. She wanted the *dueno* her son to find happiness with a wife he truly loved.

Refreshments were served, and the music grew dreamy. People began to drift off to bed, and soon only a single guitar was being played beneath the Spanish *encina* tree that spread its branches across the patio. Stars winked in a sky as dense as velvet, and the moon had waned leaving only a silvery shadow in the sky. The rumble of male voices still talking, and the music of the guitar, lent a transient peace to the night.

Romy slipped away unseen, running quickly up to bed, like a child eager for the morning to come.

The morning dawned golden and brilliant, and after a hasty cup of coffee and a buttered roll, Romy dressed herself in a Spanish lace middy blouse and a pair of pirate pants, and ran from the house to meet Luis on the foreshore ... she ran as if someone might pursue her, and it wasn't until she arrived at the lakeside that she realised she was wearing the Inca bracelet. She stared at it and wondered at the compulsion which had made her put it on this morning.

Then she saw the boat which Luis had hired from one of the fishermen. It has a pea-green sail and she broke into a smile as he held out a hand for her to jump aboard. She was light in her rope-soled shoes, almost gamine with her pony-tailed hair catching the sunlight.

Luis clenched her hand and studied the bracelet

that glinted with a pagan goldness. 'We have a food hamper and a flagon of wine. A breeze to carry the sail, and no cares, eh?'

'No cares, Luis.' She spoke gaily. 'Those we leave behind us for the day.'

'You are sure this is what you want?' His eyes were serious for a moment, studying her upraised face.

'I am very sure . . . listen, Luis, I seem to hear that beguiling voice across the lake.'

'You are full of romantic fancies,' he scoffed. 'A dreamer who refuses to awake to reality.'

'What is reality?' She gazed about her at the wonderful beauty of the morning, with a sparkle to the water and birds on the wing. She felt like the Inca maiden of legend, being taken to the island for the sacrifice of her youth and all her secret longings.

'Come, Luis, let the owl and the pussycat be away on their voyage.'

He laughed and tossed her a papaya, succulent and thirst-quenching. She ate it as the boat sailed out across the thousand silver ripples of the lake. She shut her mind to everything but the hypnotic dance of the water. She mustn't think of the future; she must like the Inca maiden pretend that after today she would still be able to feel both pleasure and pain.

Sunshine scattered itself on the lake so that it shone like a great broken opal. 'Do you mind very much, Luis, that I asked you to take me where the

Indians never go? Are you superstitious about it?'

'It has a pagan history ... the virgins were sacrificed there to the Aztec gods.'

'How cruel were their gods.' She shivered in the sunlight, and watched as the island came in sight, long and lizard-shaped, with a hump at the centre. Luis steered in against the shingle and leapt ashore. Romy followed him and stood looking about her with eager eyes ... eyes as green as the palm leaves that waved on the shore.

While Luis was busy bringing the hamper off the boat and the rug for their picnic, Romy wandered off across the silvery sand and climbed the rocks that led to the island's vantage point. Halfway up she turned to beckon Luis ... down there on the sands lay the hamper, but he was back on board the boat and steering it away from the island.

'Luis ...' His name echoed on the breeze, and the strangest fear clutched at her heart. 'Luis ...' She scrambled down the rocks and ran to the water's edge. 'What are you doing ... come back!'

He waved to her and she could see the flash of his teeth in a smile. The pea-green sail stood defiantly against the blue of the sky, and it stunned Romy to realise that she was being left all alone on this island of sacrifice.

The palm trees waved their fans with lazy unconcern above her head and she kicked at the sand in sudden temper. 'Luis, you traitor!'

'Naughty, naughty,' drawled a voice. She swung round and there by a palm tree stood a tall and negligent figure, barefooted like an Indian, black hair agleam with water, a silk shirt open to his waist and tucked into the belt of long narrow trousers.

Romy could barely believe her eyes. 'Don Delgado!'

'None other.' He strolled towards her, flagrantly attractive and supple as a panther, a lazy smouldering to his eyes that made Romy take a step backwards away from him.

'Th-the pair of you arranged it!' she gasped. 'It was a conspiracy between you ... oh, I might have guessed! Luis is too much your friend to ever do anything ... how did you get here?'

'I swam, with my clothes around my neck like an Indian.'

'All that way?' She could feel her heart beating hard beneath the lace of her middy blouse as his eyes stole over her, so deliberately, coming to rest on the bracelet he had given her.

'Did I not tell you that if you ran away from me I should come after you?'

'But ... why?'

He slowly smiled. 'There is not a soul at the *hacienda* who doesn't know why. You alone seem innocent of the reason. Tell me,' his voice softened dangerously, 'why do you wear my bracelet when you planned to look seduced by another man?'

'It's a nice chunky piece of jewellery that goes well with my outfit,' she said defiantly.

'It goes very well with your ... outfit.' Almost before she knew it he was close to her and she was tilting her eyes to look at him, at the warm, hard lips curving into a smile. She felt curiously breathless ... she wanted to run from him, but where could she go on this small strip of sand and stone to get away from him? He made her feel intolerably shy and uncertain, and as her gaze dropped away from his, she saw in the opening of his shirt the jagged scar on his right side. A feeling of faintness seemed to sweep over her, and then she was in the Don's arms, held passionately close to his golden skin and the crucifix which hung against his breast.

The touch of him, the tang of his skin, the tousled blackness of his hair, they combined to so disarm her that very little fight was left in her. She wanted to cling to him, to give love for passion, if that was all he wanted. 'No,' she breathed, 'you'd bully me day and night, make me so much yours that I'd have no freedom ...'

'Mine,' he agreed, his lips burning warm against the hollow of her throat. 'My possession.'

'Oh ... how typically arrogant!'

'Sacrificed to me instead of a stuffy museum, *mia*.'

'Th-the Ambassador's lady?'

'His lady with the tawny gold hair and the green eyes.'

'Gado ... I could never carry it off!'

'Then for you I shall refuse to be Ambassador.'

'For me?' She pulled away a few fractions to search his eyes; what she saw there made her bury her face swiftly against him. 'I couldn't let you do that. You've worked for it. You deserve it.'

'Do I, *dulce amiga*?' He crooned the words against her bright hair. 'How good of you to say so.'

And feeling him so close to her, strong and yet vulnerable, she realised the truth of what she said. He worked hard for his people, and was as generous as he was passionately just. All this she had noticed, what she had been blind to was the rather lonely man searching for love and finding it, to his chagrin, in a rebellious English girl who would keep saying that she wanted to lock herself in a museum with dead things.

'Gado, you have often called me a child.' She smiled against his warm shoulder. 'You meant I was too juvenile to be trusted with your adult feelings, didn't you? I ... I don't seem to feel juvenile any more. I feel ...'

'Unutterably sweet, dear Puritan.' His hand tilted her head against his arm and his eyes shook her heart with the look of love that burned in them. 'Did you never wonder why I travelled home on a train when I could have taken a plane? No, you are much too innocent and modest. I bribed the clerk at your hotel to tell me where you were going and when. I arranged to be on that train ... fate was kind enough to arrange the rest.'

'I always knew you were a devil,' she murmured.

'Do you mind, *amada*?' His eyes were laughing at her, but they were also loving her, and nothing mattered except that he love her. If he ever asked she would give him her soul, and perhaps she did as her lips met the sweet and dangerous ardency of his lips.

'There is one thing I should like to know, Gado. What was Carmencita doing in your arms the other night?'

'Confessing that she likes you ... that if I am to marry someone other than herself, then the "demure English Miss" should suit me well. She suits me very well.'

'She also loves you, Don Delgado.'

FREE! Harlequin Romance Catalogue

Here is a wonderful opportunity to read many of the Harlequin Romances you may have missed.

The HARLEQUIN ROMANCE CATALOGUE lists hundreds of titles which possibly are no longer available at your local bookseller. To receive your copy, just fill out the coupon below, mail it to us, and we'll rush your catalogue to you!

Following this page you'll find a sampling of a few of the Harlequin Romances listed in the catalogue. Should you wish to order any of these immediately, kindly check the titles desired and mail with coupon.

Have You Missed Any of These Harlequin Romances?

- [ ] 1031 FLOWERING DESERT
  Elizabeth Hoy
- [ ] 1100 THE BROKEN WING
  Mary Burchell
- [ ] 1103 HEART OF GOLD
  Marjorie Moore
- [ ] 1138 LOVING IS GIVING
  Mary Burchell
- [ ] 1146 THE IMPERFECT SECRETARY
  Marjorie Lewty
- [ ] 1149 A NIGHTINGALE IN THE
  SYCAMORE   J. Beaufort
- [ ] 1164 MEADOWSWEET
  Margaret Malcolm
- [ ] 1165 WARD OF LUCIFER
  Mary Burchell
- [ ] 1167 DEAR BARBARIAN
  Janice Gray
- [ ] 1168 ROSE IN THE BUD
  Susan Barrie
- [ ] 1171 THE WINGS OF MEMORY
  Eleanor Farnes
- [ ] 1173 RED AS A ROSE
  Hilary Wilde
- [ ] 1181 DANGEROUS LOVE
  Jane Beaufort
- [ ] 1182 GOLDEN APPLE ISLAND
  Jane Arbor
- [ ] 1184 THE HOUSE OF OLIVER
  Jean S. Macleod
- [ ] 1213 THE MOONFLOWER
  Jean S. Macleod
- [ ] 1242 NEW DOCTOR AT NORTHMOOR
  Anne Durham
- [ ] 1307 A CHANCE TO WIN
  Margaret Rome
- [ ] 1308 A MIST IN GLEN TORRAN
  Amanda Doyle
- [ ] 1310 TAWNY ARE THE LEAVES
  Wynne May
- [ ] 1311 THE MARRIAGE WHEEL
  Susan Barrie
- [ ] 1312 PEPPERCORN HARVEST
  Ivy Ferrari
- [ ] 1314 SUMMER ISLAND
  Jean S. Macleod
- [ ] 1315 WHERE THE KOWHAI BLOOMS
  Mary Moore
- [ ] 1316 CAN THIS BE LOVE ?
  Margaret Malcolm

- [ ] 1317 BELOVED SPARROW
  Henrietta Reid
- [ ] 1318 PALACE OF THE PEACOCKS
  Violet Winspear
- [ ] 1319 BRITTLE BONDAGE
  Rosalind Brett
- [ ] 1320 SPANISH LACE
  Joyce Dingwell
- [ ] 1322 WIND THROUGH THE
  VINEYARDS   J. Armstrong
- [ ] 1324 QUEEN OF HEARTS
  Sara Seale
- [ ] 1325 NO SOONER LOVED
  Pauline Garner
- [ ] 1326 MEET ON MY GROUND
  Essie Summers
- [ ] 1327 MORE THAN GOLD
  Hilda Pressley
- [ ] 1328 A WIND SIGHING
  Catherine Airlie
- [ ] 1330 A HOME FOR JOY
  Mary Burchell
- [ ] 1331 HOTEL BELVEDERE
  Iris Danbury
- [ ] 1332 DON'T WALK ALONE
  Jane Donelly
- [ ] 1333 KEEPER OF THE HEART
  Gwen Westwood
- [ ] 1334 THE DAMASK ROSE
  Isobel Chace
- [ ] 1335 THE RED CLIFFS
  Eleanor Farnes
- [ ] 1336 THE CYPRESS GARDEN
  Jane Arbor
- [ ] 1338 SEA OF ZANJ   Roumelia Lane
- [ ] 1339 SLAVE OF THE WIND
  Jean S. Macleod
- [ ] 1341 FIRE IS FOR SHARING
  Doris E. Smith
- [ ] 1342 THE FEEL OF SILK
  Joyce Dingwell
- [ ] 1344 THE DANGEROUS DELIGHT
  Violet Winspear
- [ ] 1352 THE MOUNTAIN OF STARS
  Catherine Airlie
- [ ] 1357 RIPPLES IN THE LAKE
  Mary Coates
- [ ] 1393 HEALER OF HEARTS
  Katrina Britt

All books are 60c. Please use the handy order coupon.

o

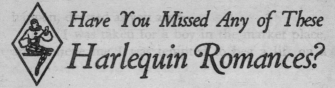

Have You Missed Any of These
Harlequin Romances?

P